ABOUT

Over two decades, Matt Pink has held a senior position within the fashion industry in Central London, working for some of the biggest brands in the world. Work hard, play harder was the formula to much of his success, but following a deep tragedy in 2013, Matt's lifestyle choices took a turn for the worse, resulting in him losing everything he had worked hard to build.

After the experience of hitting rock bottom, Matt spent the following two years climbing slowly out of the pit of despair. Step by step, he has come back fitter, stronger and healthier than ever before, and he now sees his purpose as helping others to become their best self regardless of adversity. Helping people realise their full potential in life and supporting them in removing harmful coping mechanisms and entering the wonderful world of health and well-being. If he can do it, anyone can.

BETTER ME BETTER YOU

SHARING MY JOURNEY TO HELP YOU LIVE A BETTER LIFE

MATT PINK

FUZZY FLAMINGO

First published by Fuzzy Flamingo 2021
© 2021 Matt Pink

Paperback ISBN: 978-1-7399631-4-9

A CIP catalogue record for this book is available from the British Library

Cover design and typesetting: Fuzzy Flamingo
www.fuzzyflamingo.co.uk

For my beautiful Kirsty and our wonderful tribe,
Lily, Kitty, Cooper and Raffy
You mean everything to me; I hope this book makes you proud.

In loving memory of Rocco

CONTENTS

INTRODUCTION

Everyone's always so fucking tired. You haven't slept properly so you load yourself up for the day with coffee, carbs and sugar, then you go home and eat your uninspiring dinner and sit in front of yet another TV show whilst thinking about all the shit you've got to do the following day, sipping away on that bottle to escape your thoughts and get you off to sleep, only to start the same cycle again the next day.

Everyone's always so fucking stressed. You are working tirelessly in a job you don't really like, but it pays the bills and now you feel like you are trapped and just have to exist in that place until "something better comes up" or you "come into some money". There is no way that you can do anything else with your life now because it's "too late", and it's "all you know".

Sometimes you have a moment where you realise that you've piled on a few extra pounds and it's time to go on a diet, only for that to fizzle out after a week or so and you end up back in that trap of comfort, familiarity and cake.

Sometimes you get fed up with drinking too much, so you take a little break from the booze, only for that to last as long as it is until the next social occasion arises or the next time you have a "tough day".

Sometimes you decide it's time to do some exercise, you get out and do that run or join that gym for a few sessions until the novelty wears off and you're back on the sofa again, telling yourself that you will start again next week, but you never go back.

Sound familiar?

So many of us live a life that is seriously below our potential, and the problem is we don't take the time to pause, reflect and redirect ourselves. Usually, the only time this happens is when we go through a change in our lives that is out of our control. This could be the loss of a loved one, a breakdown in marriage or, as we have all now experienced, a global pandemic.

Life gets in the way, we don't seem to have time, we are always chasing our tail. Then suddenly you're on your death bed, you have the time to reflect and you then start to regret living such a miserable life. You realise that you should have taken more risks, made things happen, seen more of the world, laughed more, looked after yourself better. Well, it's too fucking late for that then, but it's not too late now.

There is no such thing as a life manual, you are just born into this world and have to give it your best shot. You rely on what you are taught by your parents and the education you were given at school and that's it. Nobody teaches you about parenting, nobody tells you how to deal with stress, anxiety, grief or depression. You just have to do what you can when you inevitably arrive at these future obstacles.

Once you make it through the schooling system, you are conditioned into thinking that your grades and performance dictates how successful you will be in life, which is absolutely not the case. You can be whatever you want to be, you just need a clear plan and a lot of determination. No matter how tough you think your life is and how many excuses you can think of, you are the only person stopping you from achieving your dreams.

The good news is you are in the right place because I've been there. As you will go on to read, I have bounced back from the very worst of what life can throw at you, to where I am today: happy, healthy and free. I haven't done this through buying new shiny things or multiple counselling sessions, this has been done internally, through the way I think, how I act and how I feel.

This book lays out the formula that I used to transform myself into a better me, in every single way possible, financially, physically, mentally and spiritually, but most importantly as a man, as a person and as a father. I hope this book helps you on your journey as much as it has helped me.

THE CONCEPT EXPLAINED

*B*etter Me Better You seemed a very obvious name for this book, as it's not only self-explanatory, but it tells you my story and experiences, then follows it up with how I made the changes in a step-by-step guide. This eliminates the need for you to write all over this masterpiece and makes it easy for you to refer back to.

Everything in this book is written from my own experience and is designed to help as many people as possible to become aware of the possibilities that life holds ahead for you, behind the curtain of self-limitations, beliefs and habits.

I am going to take you on a journey that doesn't offer a background of deep psychology, nor does it claim to be methodology that has been proven by many over a long period of time; it's the journey that I took. The journey that took me from the darkness of despair into a life of freedom, health and happiness.

I hope this book will inspire you to think differently, to become more self-aware, to feel confident with your true self and to question the conventional journey that has been well trodden by the generations before you, and to ultimately become a better you.

There are nothing but positives you can take from this book and the thought of just one person picking this up and reading it fills me with excitement as I know the changes that lie ahead for you and the true happiness that awaits.

MY JOURNEY

For the first twenty-nine years of my life, it was pretty fucking great.

My childhood was perfect, I grew up with my parents and two sisters in a lovely house in a quaint little cul-de-sac. Every weekend I played football; my dad would be there supporting me from the sidelines every week, whilst my sisters would be in dancing shows accompanied by my mum. We would all then congregate as a family around the dinner table every evening to discuss the day's events and repeat the cycle.

I really enjoyed every part of my childhood, except school. I went because I had to, but I didn't particularly enjoy the learning side of it, nor exceed at anything other than sport, so as soon as I could leave, I did. Armed full of grades that could spell DUDE, I fell into the world of retail and, surprisingly, I loved it. Not an industry that I particularly aspired to work in, but one in which you are required to have personality over qualifications, which worked well for me.

From leaving school up until the age of twenty-three, my life consisted of working long hours, earning as much money as I could so that when the weekend came I could go out and get wasted with my friends, laugh about all the shit we got up to, then repeat the process the following week. As funny as those days were, after a fair few years of partying in the same place with the same people, it was wearing thin, so I decided I wanted a change of scenery, I wanted to go and see the world. I had no commitments or ties, and it seemed the perfect age to go and do it.

Following a string of visa applications and various jabs, I was off backpacking around the world on the adventure of a lifetime. London to Bangkok was the first leg of a journey with no fixed end date. I travelled throughout Thailand for three months, going from Bangkok down the west coast to Krabi, Phuket and Koh Phi Phi, before hopping over to the beautiful eastern islands of Ko Samui, Ko Pha Ngan and Ko Tao. When my three-month visa expired, I took the overnight train to Malaysia, moving on to Singapore before taking a flight to Australia.

I spent six months in Australia moving around from place to place and had the best time, staying in different hostels, meeting new people, drinking every day and forming memories that will last a lifetime. I impulsively took an unplanned detour to New Zealand and travelled all around both beautiful islands before heading to Fiji for a month of island hopping and getting really drunk on desert islands.

I just had the best time. I loved every part of the trip, even the travelling itself. In fact, the last leg of the trip was interesting as I flew from Fiji to LA, which was a ten-hour flight, but because of the time difference, I landed nine hours before I took off – I still can't work that one out! I travelled around the USA for a month before taking a flight back to London. After ten months of backpacking, dirty hostels and poverty, coming back to see the family, home-cooked food and a clean warm bed was amazing. Travelling really did change my life for the better, I felt as though I had survived; I left a boy and came back a man.

On my return, I immediately decided I wanted to move into central London. I grew up a thirty-minute train ride away from London, so had always been around the big city, but never thought I would have the courage to move there. However, travelling had given me so much confidence in myself and my perception of what seemed like a big scary city had changed. After spending some time alone in some actual big scary cities, London seemed like Disneyland. I started working on Oxford Street in London's West End, the busiest shopping street in the UK. For anyone who works in retail it's the ultimate challenge, a challenge that I was more than ready to take on.

London life was good, really good. Everything was going well with my girlfriend and we moved into our own flat together. Shortly after, in the February of 2009, our first child was born, Lily Pink. Lily was born at St Mary's hospital in London, famous for being the hospital of choice for many of the royal family. Princess Diana gave birth to William and Harry there, and in more recent years the princes themselves welcomed their own children into the world in the same place, and it felt like I had my very own princess.

It was the start of a new chapter in my life, one that would see me grow into the unknown world of maturity and responsibility, something I was aware I needed to take on almost as much as I wanted to. In 2011 we got married and a year later welcomed our second child and our first son into the world, Rocco William Pink. Life couldn't have been better. I was married, had two beautiful children, a boy and a girl, I was flying in my career, earning more money than I ever had, I was driving a new Mercedes and I'd even managed to buy my first house. I went into 2013 full of confidence and hope. But my life was about to change forever.

Spring had arrived and it was a beautiful sunny day in April. I had recently taken up road cycling as a new hobby and had decided to head out on a long ride to enjoy the first warm sun in what felt like forever. On my return, I arrived home to an ambulance parked outside my house, my wife running across the street and what appeared to be blankets in her hand. I could hear nothing but her piercing scream, the blankets in her arms were holding something and that something was Rocco.

He had gone down for his nap, and not woken up. I threw down my bike and got in the car to follow the ambulance to the hospital. When I arrived, the severity of the situation hit me hard. One of the senior doctors came over and told me it didn't look good, but they were going to keep trying. I remember thinking, *what are you talking about?* I couldn't believe what was happening.

I felt as though I was watching it all unfold in slow motion. There were so many people in the room, and everyone had a job, and they were all working so hard, but they were getting no response from Rocco. They started to slow down, my mind was filling with thoughts: *Why are you slowing down? What are you doing? You can't be giving up on him so quickly! Do something!* But nothing was coming out of my mouth, partly because I felt completely paralysed in shock and partly because I knew they weren't going to be able to bring him back.

The doctor came over and said the words that no parent should ever have to hear, "We have done all we can, I am so sorry." Everything stopped except the beeping of the life support machine. One by one the nurses left the room saying how sorry they were as they left. The doctor asked me if I wanted to switch off his life support machine. I leaned over, kissed his head and switched it off. He died of sudden infant death syndrome, also known as cot death, at the age of four and a half months.

Everything changed.

I was distraught, devastated, shocked, angry and just uncontrollably upset. I spent weeks just sitting still and staring into space, unaware of the people that visited, the cards that were sent or the flowers that filled the house. I lost track of everything. I didn't know what day it was and to be honest I didn't even care. My only focus was on the funeral arrangements, the gravestone and making sure I could give my boy the best send-off possible.

The day of the funeral arrived, and the venue was packed with friends and family; people had travelled from all over the country just to show their love and support, which made the day even more emotional. I made a promise to myself that I wanted to carry him in his coffin to his final resting place, not a promise that anyone should have to make to themselves. But I managed to channel all of my emotion into energy so that I could do that one thing and, trust me, I needed every single bit of it. Each step was considered, it felt like everything was happening in slow motion. All I could hear was the thud of each footstep, mixed in with the weeping of everyone around me, but I made it and I felt an enormous sense of pride in myself for doing it. I had never classed myself as a manly man before, but in that moment, I felt ten feet tall.

There isn't a job in the world that's harder than carrying your own child in a coffin and I had just completed it. My outlook on the world changed in that instant, knowing that anything that I had previously been stressed or worried about meant nothing. Now I was conditioned to be stronger and to be more resilient to life in general. It also sparked a fire inside me that changed the direction of my life. I knew I wanted to devote my life to doing something that he will be proud of me for; I had no idea what that would be and, for that moment and the months that followed, all I had in store was grief, grief that was so acute it physically hurt.

A number of weeks after the funeral I decided to return to work and try to reintegrate myself back into my own life in the hope of relieving some of the pain, but as much as I tried, I had nothing in me. My performance stagnated, my diet was worse than ever before, my sleep was non-existent, my fitness completely stopped, and I started drinking more than ever. I had always enjoyed a drink, but my relationship with alcohol changed from a want to a need.

I struggled badly day after day. The only person I could talk to was my wife, but she was going through her own agony. I tried counselling in some of the best places in London, but it just didn't feel beneficial. I felt uncomfortable talking to a stranger about the details of my own mind and the life of my precious son. For six months I was in a drunken daze, nobody could help me, and nothing was working.

In desperation I went to see a spiritualist. I never thought I would ever see a spiritualist, I thought it was a complete load of nonsense to be honest, but with nothing to lose I set off, and boy am I glad I did. I was nervous as I arrived at this lady's home. She had a lovely house and the smell of incense sticks burning hit me as soon as I got out of the car. The lady's husband greeted me and showed me into her waiting room, otherwise known as the dining room! I felt comforted as I waited for her to finish a reading with someone else. I could hear the appointment was coming to an end and I remember hearing a lot of laughing, which made me even more at ease. Finally, the lady came to greet me. She was lovely and kind and in we went to a dark, smoke-filled room, almost exactly as you would imagine it to be. Incense sticks burning, crystals displayed all around the room and calming music playing in the background.

I only had thirty minutes and there was a big alarm clock she set as soon as she started talking. I was then read a letter that was handwritten on both sides of a sheet of A4 paper. This was something she had written before I had arrived. The letter described a variety of things about my personality, career decisions and my health, all very accurate and also very positive. It made me loosen up a bit and as she continued with the reading, all of my previous sceptical thoughts slowly starting to dissolve. I was then asked if I wanted to speak to anyone in particular. Despite my newfound appreciation of the spiritual world, I still found myself not letting onto the real reason I was there. I didn't want to give her the answers,

I wanted her to prove to me that this was all real and not just a load of bollocks.

I was told I had a few people that wanted to speak to me. I instantly started to well up. "Someone on your dad's side, died in his forties, he was a road accident, wants to say hello." She then started to tell me that my great uncle was also waving, moaning at something he wasn't very happy with, but we couldn't really work out what that was. She really started to get my attention when she said your grandad is giving you a thumbs up. This was something that he was famous for within our family when he was alive, and we all used to joke about it. I started to feel tears running down my face as I became aware of a network of support I didn't know I had and the reality of the spiritual world was shining through.

The more the reading went on, the more I was losing hope of connecting with Rocco, until there was one last person who wanted to say hello, my great grandmother. This was someone I hadn't met on either side of the family, so I had no clue who it was or what she looked like, but I was all ears. The medium started to tell me that my great grandmother was desperately trying to show me something: "She is trying to show you she is holding something, she is holding a baby. She's telling me it's your baby, it's your son, it's Rocco." My darling boy was in her arms.

The medium was smiling, almost laughing as she continued to tell me in a blasé manner that he was absolutely fine. "He is a reoccurring spirit who has been here many times before. Your great-grandmother wants you to know that he's okay, he's happy and he loves you. She also keeps trying to tell me that she adores him, she is taking good care of him and she doesn't want to put him down." Hearing that he was okay and knowing that my family were taking care of him gave me a sense of comfort and relief that I longed for. I never would have thought that I would find comfort from a spiritual reading; in fact, I never thought I would even believe the spiritual world was real up until that point of my life, but now I knew, I loved it and I wanted more of it. As I left that day, I asked when I could come back again as I felt so much better. The lady said to me, "You don't need to come back, my darling, if we need you, we will come to you." Something I didn't understand until a few years later.

That experience pushed me to find something to focus on other than work. Something to help keep my mind busy. Hearing that he was okay gave me a sense of relief that I hadn't had before and that gave me the encouragement to look forward. I started running, partly because I knew it was good for the mind, partly because I had done it before and partly because I was becoming a bit of a fat bastard.

As someone who is definitely in the all or nothing category, simply running a few miles isn't something that excited me, if I'm going to do something, then I'm going to do it properly, so in 2015 I signed up for the London marathon. I wanted to run it in memory of Rocco and raise as much money as possible for a charity called The Lullaby Trust (www.lullabytrust. org.uk) that raises awareness of SIDS (sudden infant death syndrome). Running in such a huge event, raising money for such an amazing charity so close to my heart and knowing that I was running in Rocco's memory gave me a sense of purpose for the first time in a while.

I instantly became obsessed with marathon training; it was all consuming, but it helped me mentally and physically in day-to-day life. During the time I was training, we found out that my wife was pregnant, and it was another boy! Eleven days before the day of the marathon we welcomed Cooper Jay Pink into the world. Things felt as though they were starting to turn around for the better. Never would Rocco be replaced, but having another boy felt comforting. Cooper was a beautiful blond-haired blue-eyed baby, a complete contrast to Rocco with dark hair and dark eyes, it was as if the universe gave us that contrast as a way of differentiating the boys.

When the marathon day arrived, it was one of the most amazing occasions of my life. It was a dream come true to take part in such a historic event, all of my friends and family were scattered around the city at different viewpoints and the atmosphere was electric. It was a day that was charged with emotion from the moment I woke up. Walking towards the start line, I could feel myself pumping with adrenaline, but as much as I had nailed the training plan to perfection, I was completely overcome with emotion, to a point where

I started to doubt whether or not I was going to make it. I struggled to hold myself together and just couldn't stop crying. It didn't help that everywhere I looked I could see people's running vests printed with messages and names of people that they were running in memory of; the whole place felt like one big emotional family.

After a few emotional stops along the way to kiss and hug the friends and family and an incredible amount of love and support from the thousands of people all around the course, I finally made it over the finishing line and, just like that, it was all over. The whole experience just felt like a blur from start to finish. Thankfully my cousin Kelly had flown over from America to run it with me in support, and thank God she did, as I'm not sure I could have finished it without her by my side.

When the marathon was all over, I needed to keep my mind busy to distract me from the grief that was ever present inside me. We bought a brand-new house that was bigger and better than my previous home, we chose the plot and every detail of the build from floor tiles to carpet colour and kitchen design, it was really exciting. Everything was new, new house, new baby, I even started a new job. I was trying everything to get life back to where it was before, but deep down I knew it wasn't working, something was still missing.

We decided to have another baby, and we found out it was another boy! I thought that this might be the missing piece to the puzzle. Rafferty Rex Pink was born on 10th November

2016, just sixteen months after his brother Cooper. Raffy looked exactly like Rocco, dark eyes and dark hair, full of wisdom. I felt incredibly blessed to have these three wonderful kids and the two boys being so close in age was something I was incredibly proud of. But I hadn't dealt with Rocco's death and, without the focus on marathon training, I had stopped running and my grief started creeping back into my life. I started trying to deal with it the easy way, through drinking.

People kept telling me that time is a healer, and I would start to feel better further down the line, so I thought fuck it, I'm going to work harder than ever during the day and drink away the time in the evenings, then in a few years' time everything will feel much better, I will go back to some sort of normality and everything will be just fine. Bad idea.

I had always liked a drink and had grown up in a family of drinkers, but my relationship was always by choice, and it was well under control. But the more I was drinking, the more it was becoming a need rather than a want. Drinking became my coping mechanism, it was much quicker and easier than running plus it was a lot more fun, at least in the beginning. I started drinking most nights. I'd start in London with my friends, then have a few on the train on the way home, then have a few more when I got home, and before I knew it the day was done and that was another one ticked off the list as I made my way down the path towards the promise land of normality.

However, the more I was drinking, the less fun I was having and the more it was causing me problems physically, mentally and relationship-ly. This drinking thing that was supposed to be solving all my problems started to be a problem in itself.

The effect drinking was having on my sleep was one of the biggest issues. I was waking up in the night and, not being able to go back to sleep, I would then need to use stimulants just to get through the day. I had always been a one coffee a day kind of person, but it quickly started to become four, five and six. With poor sleep and a constant hangover, my diet went downhill. Reaching for beige, fast food every day helped me to limp through the day until I could have a drink and complete the new daily cycle of my life.

The drinking wasn't enough, so I started to take drugs and smoke cigarettes in a bid to give me any kind of distraction from the grief and agony I was experiencing inside. I started to hate myself for the way I was feeling all the time and I started to use it as a form of self-harm. As the months and years went on, I started to lose respect for myself, I lost respect for other people, and I started pushing myself and my relationships to the brink with not a care in the world. Nothing mattered anymore, and I was self-destructing and losing control.

The strain of losing a child plus the coping mechanisms that had evolved put a significant amount of pressure on my marriage and, unsurprisingly, it was all over in the summer of 2018. I left the family home and set off into the unknown, armed with a bag full of clothes and nowhere to live. In a strange way, I felt a sense of relief. Trying to emotionally and financially support my ever-growing family, whilst going through the immense grief of losing a child is something that was simply too much for me to handle on my own. Plus the stress of losing a child put such a significant amount of pressure on our relationship that divorce felt like the right thing to do in many ways. Having said that, it was rough, and I was rougher.

I spent that summer in a daze. With no fixed address I was sofa surfing during the week and going back and forth to see the kids at the weekend, just doing what I needed to do whilst I was ticking off the days. Not having a home to go back to gave me even more of a reason to drink, smoke and do drugs, so that's what I continued to do for a few months, dragging my life and everything in it down with me in the process. The days started to merge into one and I was often finding myself not sleeping for days on end. I was caught in a cycle that was spiralling quickly out of control. I had completely lost the will to live and would fantasise about ending it all, wishing that I could just be with Rocco.

A few weeks later, something extraordinary happened. I was at my lowest point, which some like to call rock bottom. I was standing outside the bar in Central London after work with a friend when a guy came out of nowhere and told me he needed to speak to me. At first, I thought he was asking for money or trying to sell me something, so I carried on talking to my friend and smoking my cigarette, but he kept pursuing me and gave me a bit of paper screwed up in my hand. He spoke with a very intentional manner and began to tell me I was in trouble and my bad habits were out of control.

He began to tell me there was a new girl in my life with the letter K who was very good for me. This instantly grabbed my attention as I had recently met a girl online called Kirsty. He went on to tell me that I needed to stop these bad habits. He started to tell me random facts about me and my life, he said he could see a flower that means a lot to me, I had no brothers and I have two sisters, he said I had two boys that were close in age and very small and they have a brother who died. He said I would live a long successful life until the age of ninety-eight, but only if I stopped my bad habits and regained control of my life. This conversation went on for more than twenty minutes before he abruptly left.

I was so glad my friend was with me as it was so accurate, so random and seemed to happen so quickly I'm not sure anyone would have believed me. In fact, the state I was in, I don't think I would have believed it myself. I walked back into the bar in pure shock. I still had the bit of paper in my hand, so I unravelled it to reveal it said 0 x brothers, 2 x sisters, K = Kirsty, Flower = Lily with a drawing of a star, which is exactly what I had had tattooed on myself in memory of Rocco.

It suddenly all clicked in my head. I was at the lowest point of my life and the spiritual world had come to me, just as the lady said they would. This random guy, who came out of nowhere, gave me clear instructions: you must stop your bad habits and you will live a long successful life. This may sound an obvious thing to say to a guy smoking outside a bar, but I felt like I'd been plugged back into the circuit of life. It hadn't occurred to me I could lead a long or successful life; I felt as though the life I had left was going to be very tough and fairly short, and that was something I had accepted. He gave me the confidence that it's okay to commit to the new lady in my life, Kirsty. He said, "She is very good for you and she will help you." So, I got in touch with her and within days I had moved in with her. Twice in the space of a few years, the spiritual world came to my rescue. Who would have thought that? Definitely not me.

Kirsty was exactly what I needed in my life; someone who didn't know me and knew nothing about Rocco, she was entirely independent of the situation. I found myself immediately opening up to her; night after night I would just talk, and she would listen. She must have thought, "What the fuck have I done here?" But she stuck with me and, for the first time since Rocco had died, I had someone who I felt comfortable talking to. Day after day, night after night, we sat and talked, I cried, she cried, we cried! But it was working, I could physically feel the pressure in my mind releasing with every conversation that took place.

I started to make more of an effort to look after myself. I joined the gym, started eating natural whole food, made an effort to sleep well and stay hydrated, I felt good. But it wasn't just physical improvements I wanted to make. I had an urge to learn, which is not something that I ever thought I would say, but I became obsessed with wanting to learn about anything, nothing in particular, literally anything. I felt like I needed to work that learning muscle in my mind, one that had barely been flexed for a number of years. The mind itself became something I was fascinated by, how it worked and how I could harness it to help me become a better version of myself. That led me down a rabbit hole of podcasts and YouTube videos; I even read a book, which is something I hadn't done since school, but I loved every second of it and I was hungry for more.

This new and fascinating world of personal development had made me question everyone and everything that was in my life and assess whether or not they supported me in becoming the best version of myself. One of the biggest questions I faced was around alcohol. I decided to give 'Dry January' a go in 2020, just before the world started to shut down for the coronavirus pandemic. Dry January has gained popularity over recent years in the UK, but I had never managed to give up for more than a few weeks, so doing a month was going to be a real test. Despite my new awareness, and my strong desire to be better, two weeks into the month, I found myself pouring a lager in front of the football on a Sunday afternoon. I couldn't do it and I just buckled under the pressure of my own mind.

This time was different, though; my personal development journey had taught me so much about the power of the mind and the way in which our future is determined by our behaviour today, but it had also made me more conscious of my behaviour. So, rather than just going back into my cycle of drinking, I was conscious of how I felt whilst I was drinking, what damage it was doing to my health, how poor my sleep quality was when I drank, my behaviour when I was drinking, the money I was wasting on drink. I started to realise that if I was going to achieve everything I'd said I wanted to in my life and become the best version of myself then I needed to consider something that was unimaginable beforehand: going sober.

I spent the weeks that followed flirting with the idea in my head, following people on social media that had made the jump into the world of sobriety, all the while being torn between the world of hardcore partying and complete abstinence. When coronavirus hit and the world went into lockdown, I spent the first month hoarding booze whilst everyone else was hoarding toilet paper. It was a real awakening moment as I realised that I wasn't the one in control of the relationship, alcohol was.

I spent a lot of time visualising the life I wanted to live and the person I wanted to become and, in order to achieve that, I realised that there was no place for alcohol. I was giving myself a taster of the sober life by not drinking mid-week and focusing on regular exercise, deep sleep, having a healthy diet, enjoying a clear head and better concentration. I had much more meaningful connections with people when I was not drinking and I loved how much better I was as a friend, a partner, but mainly as a father.

Between myself and Kirsty, our two daughters were at a very influential age of eleven and I wanted them to know that alcohol consumption is optional. I was determined to be a role model for them. The boys were three and four years old, so they were too young to know the difference, but that also added motivation because, if I gave up totally, they would only know their dad as someone who didn't drink, which made me really proud.

On April 21st 2020, I woke up and just decided: "Today's the day. I'm giving it up and I couldn't be happier about my decision." I had an urge to tell the world, it was like my release date from self-imprisonment. I called my parents and close friends with an air of excitement to tell them my news. Many of my friends took it with a pinch of salt, as they were all too aware of my love for drinking, as well as my previous failed attempts to give it up for any period of time let alone forever. My parents seemed to believe me, and Kirsty was right behind me, but I just knew it was over and I was done with it forever.

The weeks that followed were amazing, we had the best time together as a family. I lost weight, became fit, slept well, ate well and felt incredible. My mindset had completely changed and by removing alcohol from my life I suddenly felt free. Everything became clear and I suddenly felt a huge sense of freedom and purpose. I woke up early every single day and was bouncing out of bed with so much energy and motivation. I didn't even have anywhere to go but I was so happy alcohol was out of my life and I was free.

DISCOVER

"Anyone who stops learning is old, whether at twenty or eighty. Anyone who keeps learning stays young."

Henry Ford

We can be whoever we want to be, it's literally a state of mind, but very few people understand that.

We are in control of our thoughts and emotions, so why don't we choose happiness? Why can't we just be better?

If you want to master your own mind, first you must understand how it works.

PERSONAL DEVELOPMENT – BETTER ME

One cold winter morning, I was on my daily commute walking to take the Tube at King's Cross station in London. I had been on one of my many health kicks, which involved taking a break from the booze, hitting the gym and eating healthy food for breakfast, lunch and dinner, so I was feeling pretty good and had a spring in my step. I had also recently started listening to podcasts on my way to work rather than the repetitive choices of music that I had been reliving for as many years as I care to remember. Podcasts were great; not only were they entertaining, but in many cases I found them really inspiring and motivational.

I had been listening to them regularly for a few months, usually flitting between football, boxing and the odd bit of health and fitness, all things that interested me and subjects I have a real passion for. I found them easy to digest; they were a bit like an audio version of an autobiography, which usually consisted of hearing people's life story and how they managed to get themselves to where they are now, and usually contained some pretty inspiring stories along the way.

On this particular day, I found myself exploring my Spotify library looking for mindset-based podcasts, not a subject I had ever been interested in before. However, it was something I kept hearing people talking about on these inspirational podcasts. It was almost like everyone I was inspired by had worked as hard on training their mind as they had on their body, something that I found fascinating and made me intrigued to find out more.

I found one that lasted ten minutes, which is the same amount of time as it took me to complete my daily Tube journey, three stops southbound on the Victoria line to Oxford Circus, so it was the perfect time to try it out. Approximately two minutes into the episode, I had one thought and one thought only: this is life changing. I felt as though the guy was talking to me directly about me and my life; everything he was saying resonated hard and I was hanging on every word that was being said. He offered such small changes to the way you think that seemed so simple but so effective. Nobody in my life had ever talked to me about mindset or the power of the mind before and I found it all so new and exciting. I couldn't believe how much you could change yourself and your life just by changing your mindset.

As the podcast finished and I made my way up the stairs, out of the Tube station and onto Oxford Street, I felt like the Incredible Hulk, completely indestructible, ten feet tall. My mindset had been completely transformed by a ten-minute podcast. Absolutely nothing I had to do that day was going to be a problem, I felt so positive about my life and I had a great sense of confidence about what I was capable of achieving. I was instantly more aligned with who I really am and what I truly value in life, rather than defending my own egotistical thoughts and opinions that had formed over time. People noticed the change in me instantly, asking me questions like what had I had for breakfast and what had happened to the old Matt Pink who used to walk around like he owned the place? Something just clicked for me, I was a new man, and I was loving it.

I was calm and assured, I listened rather than talked over people and I felt like a brand new person. From that moment onwards, I dived head first into all things mindset and personal development. I looked at everything with a different mindset. I even looked at my commute as something I was grateful for – I was lucky to have such a regular amount of time per week where I could listen to podcasts and learn about different ways to improve my life – rather than listening to any old shit whilst on my boring repetitive daily commute. With that shift in mindset, my commute seemed to go by in the blink of an eye, rather than before where it felt like hours. So, I started to get off the train early and walk and spent time on my lunch break going for walks so that I could consume more and more information on bettering my life to then go and put everything into practice every day.

My desire to learn became stronger with every day that went by. As my understanding of the mind grew stronger, I grew stronger as a person and I started to feel as though I could really turn my life around. Many of the podcasts I was listening to referred to books that were recommended and talked highly about the joy of reading and how it adds another dimension to personal development, so I jumped onto that and started to note down any books that I liked the sound of and any that were recommended. Once that list hit ten books I decided to order them, all of them, and I couldn't wait to get stuck into the pile.

The first book I selected to read was *Shoe Dog* by Phill Knight, the founder of Nike. Reading was not my thing and the only books I had read since school were autobiographies by either highly successful people or legends of the sporting world, so this felt like the perfect book because he was both. The journey in itself was just mind-blowing, but the things that I really took from it were the desire to be successful, the perseverance through hard times and the consistent hard work, plus the routine that he had built himself. All very similar to the sports players themselves who had inspired my curiosity into this new world of personal development. Reading a book gave more detail to the story and what the journey looked like day to day. Now I was hooked on reading as well as podcasts, and my personal development journey started to gather pace.

Many more books followed, all consistently delivering a similar theme. They all had a clear vision in their mind; no matter how big or ambitious that vision was, they obsessed over it, visualising it daily, breaking free of their comfort zone, optimising their physical and mental health, reviewing their circle of influence and all having a daily routine. I started to realise that I could change my life and that shit got me excited. I used to think that successful people were just 'lucky' and that I was destined for a normal life, but now I was questioning everything. Why couldn't I be successful? What even is successful? I was creating more questions than I found answers, but it was motivating me to get stuck back into it day after day, night after night.

More than anything, personal development gave me the desire to want to learn, which is not something I ever thought I would say. But learning about things I was interested in was completely different to learning about things at school that I couldn't care less about. I was particularly obsessed with how the mind works, as it was all so new to me. It had never occurred to me that the thing in our heads is so ridiculously clever and important, yet we rarely harness it as a tool to improve our health, weight or fitness, instead going straight on the diet or joining the gym. But by programming the mind first, I was getting better results in every part of my life physically and mentally and it was a great deal easier. What an amazing life hack.

PERSONAL DEVELOPMENT — BETTER YOU

I bet you thought you left the learning days back in school, didn't you? Well, I thought exactly the same up until I stumbled into the world of personal development. The problem is that most of us are still scarred from our school days where we were all made to sit in the same classroom, listening to the same teachers, talking about the same shit that not many people really cared about, then we were all forced to sit the same exams in the same conditions on the same day, to be publicly judged on our results and subtly compartmentalised by grade and began our journey into the world of the workplace.

Whilst that system works well for the academic people in the world who are happy to knuckle down every day and follow the instructions of conventional archaic schooling, for people like me and possibly you? That didn't give me a particularly confident start in life, and it certainly didn't inspire me to want to continue with any learning in any way, shape, or form.

But our minds need to develop and grow, like water needs to flow, otherwise it will stagnate. Personal development is such an exciting world. We have all this curiosity and ambition locked away within our minds waiting to be released and, once you start unleashing this beast, your world will never be the same again.

The really cool thing about the world of personal development – and learning in general – in today's world is that it is all so accessible. We can learn about anything in the world at any time and by any means, which is super exciting and, unlike school, there are no restrictions. We can go out and learn about people or places around the world that we are familiar with or that actually interest us, we can learn a new language online, start a business from your living room, find out how many bricks are in the Great Wall of China, or what exactly is in a Big Mac.

The kids today are using YouTube tutorials to learn how to play video games or put on mascara, but people of a certain age (i.e. me) are still stuck in the dark ages and would struggle through the problem rather than using the tools that are readily available at the click of a button. This is making learning cool again, so don't worry about any damage to your street credibility. Learning is the new drug of choice, and we are all on this session together.

You can learn anything and it's really addictive once you start, as it's what you want to know about, it's your interest and your passion and that's something I want you to think about later on when we talk about finding your purpose. Podcasts and audiobooks are game changers in life in general, but especially the world of learning and personal development because they are super easy to absorb, usually free or very cheap and you can learn on the go, which is exactly what we need in this crazy world. But don't ever forget the power of the book, and I'm not just saying that because you are reading mine, but because there is something about a book; the look and feel as well as the smell and that feeling of accomplishment when it's complete.

With all of this new technology, it's completely eradicated any excuse that you can offer when it comes to having no time; there is no such excuse anymore. This world of information absorption has also created another reason why your excuse of having no time is extinct because everything is bitesize. Podcasts and YouTube videos can be five or ten minutes long, you can listen to your audiobook for ten minutes at a time. Just because they are shorter videos doesn't mean you compromise on quality content either – with so much competition out there, the quality of some of the content is outstanding, they make it quick and concise, often fun and engaging and it's a pleasure to learn.

I've become a learning junkie, so I tend to use podcasts for running or walking, eBooks for commuting and reading when I'm at home. I will also align the content with the most appropriate time to take it in. For example, I might listen to a motivational/inspiring podcast whilst out running, a more lightweight informative audiobook on the train and more of a serious paperback book or one that I have been looking forward to physically reading at home.

But the really juicy subject to learn is all about you and that is what personal development is. I cannot tell you how much there is that you don't know when it comes to you, and I can't describe the feeling of enlightenment once you start to peek through the curtain of your mind, body and soul, learning new information and then applying it into your own life.

You are probably thinking, "Where do I start?" Personal development is such a huge subject covering a vast amount of information, it can be very easy to become overwhelmed. Where I started my journey was understanding the basics of how my mind worked, which is truly fascinating and leaves you with such a good understanding of why you are the way you are and what you can do in order to transform your life. Then you can start to follow on with some of the more physical areas of personal development, such as leaning about gut health, or the benefits of fasting. Once you get started, you will find yourself moving towards the subjects that fascinate you the most. Once you find something new, that really connects with you, that's when you are onto a winner.

ACTION

- What are you interested in learning about?
  - o Maybe it's something that you were interested in as a child?
  - o Maybe it's a skill you have always wanted to start learning?
  - o Maybe it's another language?
  - o Maybe it's something trivial like all the capital cities of Europe or how language evolved?
  - o Ancient history or Dead Sea Scrolls?
- Whatever it is that interests you, get onto YouTube and watch a little video on it, buy a book or listen to a podcast about it, you will be surprised at how much fun you can have learning about something that really interests you and what a positive effect on your body it will have by stimulating the mind.

THE MIND — BETTER ME

The thought of looking into how the mind works wasn't something I had ever particularly wanted to do or something I thought I would be able to understand, but my journey of personal development led me into it, and I found it all fascinating. I couldn't believe that I had gone so far into my life without even knowing how the most powerful part of my body works.

My interest in mindset sparked after listening to that mindset podcast on my Tube journey. The idea that you could choose how you want to feel was alien to me. I had gone all of those years just working hard and hoping for the best in life, but now I was thinking differently, I was waking up and deciding how my day would go and how I would feel at the end of it. I remember in the early days of my new mindset discovery, I decided that I was going to own the meeting I was attending that day and that I was going to have full control of the situation; from where I sat to how I spoke, it was all planned in my head and I knew that I would come out of it feeling like people would have noticed the change in me, and they did.

This was the start of an exciting new world for me. How had I only just discovered how important my mindset is to everything in life? I started immersing myself in more and more literature, videos and podcasts on mindset and how elite sportsmen and women harness the power of the mind better than all their competition to help them get and stay at the very top of their game. I started to notice that it wasn't just sports people that had the strongest mindset, it was all kinds of influential people, including actors and authors. They all shared the same elite level mindset; they knew what they were going to do, and they didn't stop until they got there.

These people are just normal people with a clear vision. Something really connected with me when I realised this and I thought to myself, "What am I doing with my life, working all the hours under the sun, spending my free time drinking and socialising, eating a shitty diet and turning into a middle-aged dad, accepting the ailments that come with the territory of that lifestyle, embracing the extra pounds building around the waistline and priding myself on having such a glamourous social life. Fuck that, I want to do something with my life and everything is going to change, and it starts now."

Learning about the mind gave me more of an understanding of what I can do in my life going forward, but the real game changer for me was learning how the subconscious mind works and why I am the way that I am.

The subconscious mind is formed from childhood right up to the present day and is created by all of the influences and experiences I had along the way. From the very first time I was told not to do something as a two-year-old child, the shaping of my personality began. The food I enjoy, the way I talk, my favourite sports team, what I put on my pizza, it's all been influenced by my environment, my upbringing and the people who are closest to me. In other words, the man I am today is a version of myself that has been conditioned from external influences throughout my lifetime and it's not necessarily reflective of who I truly am, at soul level.

This made a lot of sense to me, as I had always wondered why I felt out of alignment with myself. I felt as though I didn't belong in certain places, or wondered how I managed to become friends with certain people, or how I got myself into situations that I knew I didn't belong in. That feeling of misalignment and confusion had been building more and more since I had reached my thirties, but I didn't know what it was. I thought perhaps it was to do with my ongoing grief, or because I was making the transition from young adult into middle age, so I just carried on trying to wade through life and hoping for the best.

Once I discovered how the subconscious mind worked and why I was the way I was, it all made sense. I realised that the person I thought I was isn't actually me, that's just who I had developed into because of my conditioning and upbringing. That was why I felt so frustrated with myself, that was why I struggled to understand myself and that was why I punished myself with alcohol and drugs. Finally, I understood it all. It felt like a weight had been lifted and I had been slapped round the face with a reality check.

Now that I knew that, I had an urge to question everything that I thought I liked and everything I thought I was. From really big things like where I want to live, to the smallest of things like how I take my coffee. I listed all my favourite places to go, things to eat, pastimes and hobbies, you name it, I wrote it. I questioned them all individually and asked myself, 'Do you really like that or is that a result of your subconscious programming?' More often than not, I was finding that the choices I was making were not choices I necessarily liked or really wanted, they were just what I had always chosen or what I was conditioned into liking.

I remember one of the first examples I discovered about myself was my choice of curry when having a takeaway. Not a life changing discovery but one that stands out in my mind. My dad has ordered the same curry throughout my life anytime we were to get an Indian takeaway, a hot and spicy chicken madras. For as long as I could remember, I have ordered the same curry every time, a hot and spicy chicken madras. I battle my way through the pain as the spice takes over my entire mouth, forcing myself to get through to the end only to sit in pain for ten minutes afterwards. What was I doing? Why do I do that to myself? I laughed as the reality started to kick in of just how many things I do that I don't actually enjoy doing and how much fun I was going to have shedding this artificial load.

I went on a mad one, continuing to question everything and feeling ready to become a new man at the same time. I had realised that the subconscious programming, alongside the acute grief I was going through, had turned me into someone I didn't like very much, and I was happy to leave him behind and create a new me. One by one the changes happened and with each decision I started to feel better, more confident and, most importantly, more myself.

Every change I was making was helping me become a better person. My newly found self-awareness led me to become much more conscious about other people; it's like I had rediscovered what it was like to be truly kind and considerate to other people and listen to what they have to say. Definitely a skill that was long lost to me. I was also now conscious of what I was doing to my body, my health and even the planet. I don't know where it all came from, as I had no regard for any of it previously. I guess you could call it enlightenment or a spiritual awakening, but it could also be that I was on a journey to becoming the person I really am underneath all of the layers of conditioning. Whatever it was, it felt good, and I felt as though I was on the path to alignment with who I really was, in my soul.

17

I wanted to make some big changes, but I knew it wasn't going to be easy. I had read about something called neuroplasticity, which is basically a technical term for how your brain adapts once you make changes in your life. This was a huge discovery for me as I thought that I was the way I was and that was that. But learning that the mind can be reprogrammed over time and I could be the one to choose how it was going to change was exciting. I realised that I could become whoever I wanted to become, my mind would adapt to any thoughts, behaviours, or actions that I would take on a consistent basis, and all I needed to do was make the changes and stick to them.

I took a break from drinking and started running instead, I started eating a plant-based diet and I decided that I was going to make better decisions every single day and see where I could take myself. It was all easy to begin with, but the subconscious mind likes familiarity, it doesn't like change. That's why I got that voice in my head that just wanted me to stay in my comfort zone and do what is familiar. But having the knowledge of how it all works within my mind changed the game. Now I was able to observe the thought I was having, realise that it was just my subconscious mind trying to keep me in my familiar comfort zone, ignore that thought and carry on building the strength in my new neural pathways, whilst weakening the old ones.

By learning about the mind, albeit on a basic level, I managed to overcome the inevitable hurdles that arose, managing to leap over each one and gain confidence and momentum at the same time. I also had the ability to think things through, which isn't something I had ever done before. For instance, I would fantasise about having a beer, but then I would say to myself, okay, then what? So, you have your beer, then you have another one, then where do you go and what happens next? How will you feel the next day? Does that align with who you are or is that the behaviour of the old version of yourself?

I knew that the subconscious mind just wanted to pull me back into my comfort zone, but if I gave in then my future would be very predictable because it would just be a repeat of everything that I had done in my past; and that wasn't something I was prepared to go back to, no matter how strong the calling was.

THE MIND – BETTER YOU

Now I'm not claiming to have a degree in neuroscience, but I am going to explain what I learnt in a very basic form and honestly this shit blew my mind.

When we are born into this world, we are a beautiful new soul full of life and love, but what happens as we make our way through childhood is that we start to get told what to do, and what is right and wrong. That may be as simple as being told not to touch something when you are a baby, but that is where it all starts. We are learning what is right and wrong from another person's perspective, not necessarily what is right and wrong from our own and, whilst we absorb all of this information, we are hard wiring it into our subconscious mind, and it is forming our character and shaping the way we behave.

Your subconscious mind isn't actually you. It's been created by all of your past experiences, feelings and emotions, but it's not you. Your conscious mind is you; it knows what it wants to do but is usually out-muscled by its bigger brother the subconscious mind, as that powers our thoughts 95% of the time. For example, you may want to stop smoking because consciously you know it's bad for you, but even though you know that and you have the desire to want to stop, it's ingrained in you as a habit and it's not that easy to change.

Your subconscious mind will always use past experiences in your life to predict the future. For example, when you plan a holiday you will get the feeling of excitement, which is based on a previous trip that gave you that feeling. When you wake up on Christmas morning, you have that feeling that only Christmas morning can provide, which is because of the feelings that you have had before. But when you are heading into that meeting on a Monday morning that you hate going to, guess what, your brain will release those negative chemicals that it always produces, and you will have the same experience you always have.

The problem here is that you are living a life based on past experiences, which means you are only going to live a life that will bring you more of the same; in essence, you are living a life of limited possibility and your future is very predictable. The more we live this life of repetition, the more we strengthen the neural pathways in our brain, making it more and more difficult to change. The other problem is that a lot of the thoughts that we learnt as part of our upbringing can be self-sabotaging and negative, so not only are we living a life based on other people's influences, but a lot of them aren't even helpful!

Our conscious mind is where all of our creativity comes from, our ideas, our hopes and dreams. It's the real you. But it's not strong enough to make these things a reality alone. In order to achieve these dreams and creations, we need to use our conscious mind to reprogramme our subconscious mind. It all sounds pretty complicated, and to some degree it is, but trust me, if I can get my head around it, then you definitely can, and here's how.

The first step is awareness, you need to be aware of what your subconscious mind is and why it exists. Now hopefully I have just provided a basic description of it, but if you want to look into it further by much more qualified people then get some books or watch some videos on YouTube. Dr Joe Dispenza is the main man in this field for me.

When you are aware of how the subconscious and conscious minds work, you can start to observe your own thoughts, habits and beliefs. As they say, you can't read the label if you are inside the jar and now you can read it in all its glory. At this point you create a space between you and your own thoughts; this is the moment of realisation that you are not your thoughts, you are you.

Now that you can see how it all works from outside the jar, you can start to challenge your own beliefs. You will catch yourself instantly reacting to a situation or comment in the way in which you usually would; you can pause, think and change your reaction based on the way you want to react and not how you have always done so.

This is where you start to step into the unknown and move away from your past self. But your subconscious mind isn't just going to obey your new command, it's going to be pissed off, as all it wants to do is live a safe and secure life based on what it knows, and it hates anything that will risk that. So, you will start to hear voices in your head challenging you. "Why did you say that? You can't do that, you aren't good enough to do that, you will fail if you try that." And at this point it is a lot easier to listen to your subconscious mind than to carry on. That's why people are great on a diet for a week and then go back to their previous bad habits because they are powered by the subconscious mind. It's the same with starting at the gym and not going after the first month, then you go straight back into that cycle of predictability, your future will be based on your past experiences and your life will be very predictable.

ACTION

- Listen to a podcast on mindset. I recommend The Mindset Mentor by Rob Dial as a great place to start.
- Watch a video on the subconscious and conscious mind. I recommend anything by Dr Joe Dispenza.
- Write down everything that you believe in and question every single one honestly. A great way of doing this is to write a list of everything you enjoy and put a question mark at the end of each one, i.e. I enjoy chicken madras?
- Choose how you want something to go, whether that be a meeting at work or a conversation with a friend, maybe even a trip with your kids. Think it through before it happens and decide on the emotions that you want to feel and how you want them to feel and go and get it.

THE EGO — BETTER ME

I had always been a bit of a class clown at school, resulting in people laughing at the stupid things I would get up to, prompting me to do more stupid stuff to gain the same level of gratification. I would rather get the laugh from the crowd than the reward from a teacher because it made me feel more important and valued to be a well-liked person than a successful student.

I carried that persona with me throughout school and into the workplace. Always a big personality who liked pushing the boundaries, happy to take risks, confident in anything I set my mind to. When I left school, the only job I could get was in retail and my personality traits meant that I was perfectly suited to it. I loved being in front of customers, I had the confidence to sell anything to anyone and I loved the fact that I was good at something, and it was all great for the ego.

It wasn't long before I was getting promotion after promotion, earning more money than some of my friends that had got straight A grades in school. I started buying designer clothing and expensive trainers, then flash cars with personalised number plates. I thought I was invincible and felt as though I was achieving a level of success that nobody at school would have thought possible, which made me even more motivated to kick on.

Getting into my twenties, I started to feel a bit differently about my life. I started to realise that every time I bought a new car or a new TV it felt good for a few days and then I just wanted the next one, a bit like a kid opening presents on Christmas day. When I decided that maybe it's time to do something a little bit different with my life and I went travelling around the world for a year, I started to feel more connected to myself than ever, I started to feel happier than ever, but the strange thing about that was that I had absolutely nothing to my name. I had sold my car to fund the trip and I was living on about five dollars a day.

All of the fancy clothes were left behind, I was sleeping in beach huts surrounded by nothing but lizards and palm trees, I didn't even watch TV for months. I felt amazing and, when I returned home, I was a different man. Something inside me had changed, I knew that there was more to life than having things, I knew that there was pleasure in spending time alone, away from the crowds, but I also knew that the real me isn't this loud, attention-seeking character that had formed over the years before. The real me is a sensitive soul that has a lot to give, but I just didn't know how to pull him out.

When I returned from my travels, I went back to retail as that was all I knew, but I moved into central London and wanted to rebrand myself as this new, mature version of myself, Matt Pink 2.0. Always maintaining that edge of confidence and character but in much more of a refined way. It seemed to work well, and I was quickly back onto the career path, this time in much more senior roles for some of the world's biggest brands.

Life was going well up until April 2013 when Rocco died. All of my personal progress dissipated in an instant. When I went back to work, I went straight back to my default setting of ego focus. All of the maturing that I had done on my travels, and all of the work I had previously done on figuring out that things don't equate to happiness were out of the window. I went on a mission to earn as much as I could and throw it around in a bid to make myself feel better. I was buying cars way out of my price range, buying holidays I couldn't afford and spending thousands of pounds on nights out, all because my ego took over. I didn't want people to think that I was a failure and that I was weak, so I thought the only way to behave was to be more lavish than ever before and show the world that nothing was going to keep me down.

For the years that followed, I just kept pushing harder in every direction, putting insurmountable pressure on every part of my life. My relationships with friends and family were pushed to their limit, my finances were spiralling out of control as I continued to try and protect my ever-growing ego. I was feeling the effects physically as I struggled to put on a brave face to the world, until one day it all blew up and my marriage was over.

Kicked out of the family home with nothing but a bag of clothes, I had finally lost everything. Strangely, I felt a great deal of relief; not that the marriage was over, but that it was all over. That whole act that I had been keeping up for so many years was finished. I felt like I had gone back in time to that beach hut in Thailand, where I was living on five dollars a day. That's when I knew that I had to leave that life behind forever. I knew that the person I had pretended to be for so long was now gone, for good. However I was to rebuild from there, I would not be focused on the things I had, but more focused on who I am and what I stand for.

Once I met Kirsty and dusted myself off a bit, I started to really focus on myself and who I wanted to become in life. Once I started reading and learning about the subconscious mind, it all made sense to me. My ego was a result of my subconscious programming and conditioning from other people. Throughout my schooling years and in my early years at work, I had just followed the path that gave me the quickest return and did more of what brought more success and less of what didn't. But I never considered to check if that aligned with who I really am as a person, in my soul. I just followed what I thought would be the best path to success, but even my interpretation of what success is was wrong. Success for the ego-driven Matt Pink was big houses, fancy holidays and designer clothes. I had done a bit of all of that and none of it had made me feel satisfied, it was like chasing the horizon.

The more I was peeling back the layers of conditioning, the more I was dissolving my ego. I spent so many years of my life trying to impress other people that I had completely lost who I was as a person. When I was living so far out of alignment with myself, I was becoming frustrated and stressed out with the act that I had to keep up. That then led to coping mechanisms like alcohol and drugs, which then led to a problem of its own. The ego will never be satisfied and that's a fact.

I felt like someone had woken me up from a twenty-year nightmare and now it was all over. All of a sudden, I felt grateful for everything that I had in my life, rather than constantly striving for the next thing. The more I shed my old ways, the more excited I was getting about my new direction and the more I was enjoying living in a state of freedom and peace.

THE EGO – BETTER YOU

Look at yourself in two parts. First of all you have you, the true you, the spiritual you that is connected to everyone and everything in the universe. Then you have the ego, which prioritises everything that can be experienced from the five senses of the body, taste, touch, sight, smell, hearing. The reason we were given senses was to help us survive and to perform the basic tasks of life. For example, we were given our sense of taste to avoid eating the wrong thing and we were given our sense of touch to reproduce. But over time we have evolved to be greedy and these things that were once basic needs of the human species are now being prioritised and glamourised, as you can see in the food industry with the millions of places to eat all around the world, and in the sex industry which seems to be getting bigger and more accessible every year.

What this means is that we are all focusing more on the things we can experience with our senses rather than what we

30

experience as a spiritual being. We spend our lives tirelessly trying to get more stuff, earn more money, eat more food, have more sex, climbing all over each other in the process, causing great deals of pain and suffering to one another in the process. The crazy thing is that we are all tirelessly chasing an infinite horizon that will never provide the level of satisfaction you think it will in the first place.

We have become so obsessed with looking our best or having the best things that we are all drifting further away from who we really are and losing touch with what we really want. What kind of world would it be if we all look the same, hang out at the same places and buy the same stuff?

We are all uniquely brilliant beings that are born into this world as a beautiful soul, destined to do great things in the world, but the more time goes by, the more we are conditioned and programmed with layers and layers of limiting beliefs and behaviours that cover up our shining soul. The longer that goes on, the more we start to believe everything we have been taught is who we are, that you are that character and the more you will fight for everything that character stands for.

Living like this is exhausting and futile, so if you are serious about becoming a better you, then you need to be ready to start dissolving that ego. That process can only begin once you are aware of what the ego is and how it is holding you back in your life. Then it's a case of tapping into who you really are, at soul level. Then you are on the beautiful journey into enlightenment and freedom.

You can choose to stay on the ego path, but just ask yourself if you have ever really been satisfied so far? At what cost to your physical and mental health are you prepared to go to in order to get that new car or a promotion at work? Do you really want to carry on living a life of comparing yourself with other people? You should also ask yourself whether or not you want to stay on a path that will only give you a limited level of progression and success, or do you want to enter the world of pure possibility? The crazy thing is that once you start to align yourself with the universe and stop wasting so much time and energy on chasing everything you have ever dreamed of, guess what happens? You will start to receive everything you have ever wanted in the first place.

There are so many parts to the ego, it is not practical or effective to dissolve all of it at once, nor is it possible that you could do so. The game is to detach yourself from your limiting beliefs, questioning your thoughts at all times and observing your ego's reaction to situations. Ask yourself how you really feel about this situation, rather than what the automatic ego response is. The more you detach yourself from the ego, the easier it becomes and the more exciting it gets.

ACTION

- The first step to dissolving the ego is to be aware of it in the first place, so now that I have outlined the basic overview of what it is, can you start to detach yourself from your ego and separate yourself from your thoughts?
- Write down the last time you were triggered by someone or something, and sit with it to understand why that was. Because that person who cut you up in traffic may be what you think caused you to react, but when you dig a little deeper you will find it started way before any specific incident.
- Practise gratitude daily. Whether it's just a moment when you wake up or before you go to bed, take a second to be grateful for all that you have.
- Be in the present. The ego loves to keep us regurgitating the past or worrying about something in the future that hasn't even happened yet, so whenever you catch yourself in the past or the future, pull yourself into the present moment by focusing on your breath or something nearby.

PURPOSE – BETTER ME

When I was a boy, the only question I got asked about my future was 'what do you want to be when you grow up?' My answer was always a footballer and that was it. When I realised that wasn't going to come to fruition, I didn't have a plan B. Nobody ever sat me down and asked me about my purpose in life and tried to extract what I enjoyed doing or what I was interested in, it just didn't happen back in my day. You went to school, were told to get good grades and how that went would determine what job you could get and therefore how successful you would be.

Who am I to decide what my purpose is? I got poor grades at school, so therefore I got whatever job I could and just got on with grinding out the rest of my working days trying to do the best I could do. That was my thought process, that was what I was told, so that's just what I did. It wasn't until my journey of self-discovery and my shift in mindset that I started to realise that finding my purpose is something completely different altogether.

It was only because of my personal development journey that I found out what living a life of purpose meant. I soon realised that the lifestyle of working all the hours under the sun and spending my time and money in the bars of London's West End certainly wasn't it. Although I had some incredible experiences and was fortunate to enjoy what I did for a living, the idea of having a purpose was exciting, so I went on a mission to find it.

There is a lot of information available on how to find your purpose in life, whether that's online, in podcasts or in a good old-fashioned book, information is not hard to come by. It seemed like all of the information I found through various avenues all asked the same kind of questions:

- What are you good at?
- What does the world need?
- What could you earn money from?
- What do you love doing?

I struggled to figure out what I was good at. Drinking? What does the world need? I don't know! What could I earn money from? No idea. What do I love doing? Erm, drinking? I was stuck in a mental prison, thinking that all I had to offer in life was what my previous lifestyle had consisted of, working hard and playing harder.

I was becoming more and more frustrated at the fact I couldn't find my purpose. I am a very task-driven, fast-paced guy and I just wanted to find out what my purpose was, tick it off and get on with doing it. Then I read something that changed the game completely. It said you will struggle to find your purpose by going out and looking for it, just focus on looking after yourself and allow it the space to come to you.

It said that self-care is imperative for finding your purpose as you need to give yourself time to slow down and be at one with yourself, your thoughts and your emotions. You need to become the best version of yourself and do the best job possible at every single task you do throughout the day. Become mindful and present as much as possible and your purpose will find you. It all sounded a bit fluffy to me initially, but when it sank in, it really hit home. I had already started to make all of these changes and was on the right path, but I was still mentally clinging onto my past, thinking I was the same person I had always been, abusing my body, never giving myself time, and running around like a mad man.

That moment of realisation was just what I needed. I just had to let go of who I was before and settle into the new version of myself, the better version of myself. The changes were already happening. I was already on this journey of personal development and was really enjoying learning about myself and my mindset. I had a new love for reading, which gave me some time to be with myself and to slow down. I had swapped drinking for running. My nutrition was better than ever with my newfound love for plants and that in turn had led to me sleeping well. I had even dipped my toe into the world of spirituality by using some guided meditation videos online. I was on the right path.

Giving up drinking was the change that made the biggest difference to my life. That was the catalyst that allowed the other changes to happen. I had read lots of books about going sober and they all mentioned how much time you get back in your life once you stop drinking. I couldn't get my head around it because it's just a few drinks in the evening. But it's not; you get every evening back, then you get every morning back, plus you are more productive every day as you are thinking clearly, sleeping well and eating better. All of the changes I needed to make to look after myself were all happening because I stopped drinking and I started to feel like I was unstoppable.

Running became my new addiction and I found that the more I was running, the more the fog was clearing from my mind, and I started to be able to think forwards rather than looking back. Every time I came back from a run, I had new ideas about what my future could look like and what my purpose could be. Some of my early ideas were pretty wild. I thought at one point I wanted to own an ice cream hut in Thailand! But the more I ran and the more I was looking after myself, the closer I knew I was to finding my purpose.

I was changing day by day, looking better, feeling better and just being a better person. People started to ask me what I was doing as I was literally becoming a better person by the day. When I was talking to people about the changes I was making, I felt as though I could see behind their eyes that they wanted to do the same thing but didn't know how, so I was giving them advice here and there. I found that by supporting other people, it was adding another string to my bow, one which I had never really had before, and I started to feel a sense of purpose.

Then one day, whilst out on a run, it all came together and clicked in my mind. Why don't I write a book about myself? I could share my journey in order to help as many people as possible. I have been through the most tragic experience possible, resulting in me going down a path of self-destruction, which subsequently resulted in me losing everything I had worked so hard to build. But I have picked myself up from rock bottom, decided that enough is enough and I am rebuilding myself to be better and stronger than ever. I had to figure all of this out for myself, there was no blueprint that I followed to have a better life, but I have managed to significantly improve every single area of my life, so why don't I share that path with other people that may need it.

The very next day, I purchased a bright pink pad of paper and got to work, doodling all of my ideas, sketching out different titles and just getting excited about the thought of my story inspiring other people to change their lives. It gave me a feeling that I hadn't had before, it gave me a sense of purpose. There it is: purpose.

PURPOSE – BETTER YOU

Finding your purpose can be so confusing and, at times, infuriating. But the one thing you can hang onto is the fact that we all have one, it's just that some of us need to work a lot harder than others to find it.

The first thing to focus on probably isn't what you would expect to hear, but it's very important: it's you. If you are serious about finding your purpose, then you need to allow yourself to be in the best condition to receive it. It's all very well following the questions like, what am I good at, and what does the world need, but you won't be able to find your purpose if you are trying to answer these questions whilst chowing down on a cheeseburger in front of the TV. Your physical health needs to be as good as your mental health, and if you can shoehorn a sprinkling of spirituality into the mix then you are onto a winner.

Now when I say good physical health, don't worry, I don't mean you need to lose a ton of weight and live on lettuce leaves before your purpose appears, I mean putting good food into your body that will get your body working at its best. The same applies to your mental health; you need to use the power of the mind and understand how it works in order to help you improve your mental health and give yourself a bit of space between you and your thoughts. By spirituality, I mean being more present, spending more time outdoors and more time sitting with your own thoughts. We will cover more of this later in the book, but I just want to make it clear at this point that spirituality isn't always what you think it is.

It is important not to get confused with your purpose and your profession, they can be different things. Your purpose is what you are on this planet to do and it's usually something that involves giving back, supporting, or helping others. Your profession is what you do to earn a living. In many cases you can combine the two and that makes for a match made in heaven, but it's okay to do both.

You may have heard of the phrase 'your pain has a purpose'? This was certainly true in my case, so it's a great idea to reflect on what has given you pain before and how you can change that pain into purpose. For example, you have overcome a skin condition and now have an understanding of what caused it and how to treat it, therefore you have knowledge and first-hand experience in that field, meaning that you can now harness that pain and provide a service to other people that are suffering.

I am a huge fan of running, as for me personally that's when I get to do some thinking and that's when I have my greatest ideas. You don't have to run, it could be a walk or even a drive, as long as you are alone and have some time to think in peace then it's a great opportunity for things to appear.

ACTION

- Take a break from drinking.
- Move your body more, walking or running are great for finding your purpose.
- Take time out for yourself and enjoy some mindful moments, whether that's spending time outdoors, breathing exercises or meditating.
- Follow what you enjoy doing, even if that path seems like it's never leading to your purpose. I had a love for reading that came out of nowhere, which led to me writing a book of my own, but I would never have thought that would happen.
- Try the ikigai method: write a list of what you love, what you care about, what the world needs and what you can get paid for. If there is anything that crosses over on all four of the lists, follow it, as that could be the path that leads you to your purpose.

CREATE

"The best way to predict your future is to create it."

Abraham Lincoln

Now we understand why we are the way we are, we can start on the fun part. Designing your future.

VISUALISATION – BETTER ME

Cristiano Ronaldo, Connor McGregor, Will Smith and Jim Carrey are all very successful heroes of mine that have one thing in common. Visualisation. They decided what it was that they wanted to achieve in their life, they visualised it over and over again so clearly in their mind that it felt as though it was already happening in real life, then they went out and worked harder than anyone else to get it.

My earliest memories of visualisation were from about seven years old. I would lie in bed thinking about playing football and visualise how many goals I was going to score, and how I would score those goals. I would put myself into scenarios and play it out in my head as if it were real. I would practise in my head kicking the ball into the top corner of the net over and over again, adjusting my angles to ensure the perfect connection from foot to ball. Aside from that, I don't really remember visualising much else.

The thing is, I didn't know that visualisation was a thing, it was just something that I would do when I was passionate about something because it would consume my mind and I have a strong desire to win. I never knew that it was a tool that can be used to proactively support any dreams I had in any part of my life; if I had known that when I was younger, my life could have taken a much better direction. I knew that I wanted to have kids, get married and have a nice life and that was what I had achieved, but then what? I hadn't thought about what a nice life looked like outside of my next materialistic milestone.

I wasn't specific with my longer-term vision and had never even given it much thought, I certainly hadn't visualised it. I just assumed my life would consist of earning as much money as I could to buy a house, pay it off and retire, with a few holidays along the way. After all, who was I to dream of living a life full of wealth and success? I hadn't done well at school, and I was told that if you don't do well at school you will struggle in life. I assumed that wealth and success came to only those who excelled academically, not people like me. The only way someone like me could live that life is if I was lucky, maybe won the lottery or something. But other than that, I was set on living a life of mediocracy, trying my best to succeed professionally, but in the back of my mind feeling like it could all be taken away from me and I was somewhat undeserving of success.

Once I started my personal development journey and discovered all of these successful people who harness the power of the mind to become hugely successful in their field, I started to flirt with the idea of visualisation myself. Learning about the restraints of my subconscious programming and the evolution of the ego made me realise that I was living my life stuck in a world of self-limitation. Learning about creating a vision and the power of visualisation was a profound moment of realisation for me; suddenly I felt excited about the potential limitless future, I felt a sense of confidence that had been missing for so long.

I felt as though someone had removed the ceiling and all I could now see was the sky above me. That was it, I decided that I was no longer going to live my life the way everyone else does, grinding away at a job just to earn money to put food on the table and a roof over our head. Working to fulfil someone else's dream, only getting a few weeks a year off to spend with my family. Although I was good at my job and enjoyed what I did, it's not what I was put on this planet to do, and I needed to think bigger.

I decided that I was going to give this a go, so I did a lot of research and found someone called Robert Hisee, the UK's number one unconscious mind therapist, and I loved his approach to visualisation. I got in touch with him as I was so intrigued about how I could learn more about my own mind as well as wanting some coaching on how to visualise. He kept the process simple, told me that the first step is to close your eyes and focus on your breathing, or even some music. Either way, you need to focus on something to keep you in the present moment. Then you need to allow your thoughts to glide through your mind, just acknowledge them and let them go; once they start to slow down, you can start the process of visualisation.

I closed my eyes and let my mind go. I allowed myself to visualise what my future looks like, without limitations. Who do I want to become, what do I look like in twenty years' time, what lifestyle do I have, who am I spending time with, what am I wearing, what do I eat, where do I live? The voice in my head kept interfering, giving me all the reasons why I couldn't live that lifestyle: How are you going to afford it? What will you do for a living? You don't know how to do anything else. But I was in charge, and after learning that I am separate from my thoughts and that my limiting beliefs weren't even real, the tables turned. Every time they popped up, I would simply smile and ignore them.

I focused on what matters the most to me, what I like doing and how I like to feel, rather than the materialistic side of what I want to drive or where I want to live, as I had recently learned that 'things' do not equal happiness. I had no agenda, I just let my mind wander and a picture started to gather; the longer I was visualising, the clearer the picture was and the greater the detail.

My hair is grey, my shirt is blue, and my sleeves are rolled up revealing a gold watch. I am surrounded by my children and their children. Everyone is laughing and having fun outdoors at a BBQ on a terrace with lights and lanterns all around. I am fit and healthy, tanned and happy. We are at our house, which is in Spain. We live there most of the time when we are not in our house in the UK. I love to be in the sun and like running and cycling in the sunny Spanish countryside. We all eat a healthy Mediterranean diet with lots of fresh fruit and vegetables. The kids come over regularly and use our villa as a second home. I can smell the summer air mixed with the scent of the BBQ and I can hear the noise of my joyful family talking over each other in the way that large families do. I feel proud of myself and what I have created, and I am surrounded by love.

I must have been visualising for around forty-five minutes. I felt so energised and content as I opened my eyes, as if the experience had happened already. I felt so connected to that image, as if I'd had a glimpse into my future, and I felt so excited to get on and create it. I didn't know how it was going to happen, I didn't really care how it was going to happen, I had the confidence in the process and the trust in the universe that if I kept on practising it, then it would just come to me.

Now I use visualisation all the time. Every single day I am visualising the man in the blue shirt, but I am also using it for as many things as possible. This book started as a thought in my mind one day when I was running. That night I lay in bed visualising it, thinking about how I will feel when it is released, visualising it being sold around the world. The next day I started to research how to become an author, and now here you are reading it. I have also started to use visualisation for my running, which has been incredible for my progress. Before I head out on a long run, I will run it all through in my head, thinking about how I am feeling at each mile marker and what my pace is like. If I start to feel weak at a certain distance, I will wind myself back a mile and rerun it in my head again until I feel strong, then move onto the next mile. I do this until I have visualised the entire run from start to finish and have felt strong throughout.

VISUALISATION – BETTER YOU

Without a vision of the future, you will inevitably fall back into the habits of the past, and if that happens then you are in for a very predictable future. You have the power to create the life that you dream of and become the person you want to become. You are no longer the victim of your past, you are the creator of your future. All of those limiting beliefs are out of the window and your future is in your hands.

Let's think about this for a minute. We have put a man on the moon, we fly around the world in aeroplanes, we hold virtual meetings globally, we can speak directly to our friends and family at the touch of a button. All of these things started as an idea in someone's head. These people weren't special, they just had a vision, and they became obsessed with achieving it.

There are three stages that I use when using visualisation. First, you need to get yourself feeling nice and relaxed and in the zone. You can't just pull over on the side of the road, close your eyes for two minutes and visualise a red sports car, you need to feel nice and calm and in the right environment. Plan your time in and make sure you are comfortable, and you won't get interrupted. Sit up straight as it provides a clear path for your spine and airway. Focus on your breath and bring yourself into the present moment. Your mind will naturally want to drift, and it will pop up with different thoughts and ideas, but just acknowledge them and bring your focus back to your breath. Once the thoughts start to slow down, take a few deep breaths, feeling the sensation of each breath going through your body. When you are comfortable and relaxed you can start the process of visualisation.

You may have something specific that you want to visualise and attract into your life, but you may also want to just let your mind lead you in whatever direction feels natural, just as long as it's not trying to get you visualising your past. Remember that you really want to visualise the life that you are living. Don't worry about how you get there, that will all come, but the first step is simply to visualise yourself living the lifestyle of your dreams, what can you see, what can you hear, what can you touch? Look for as much detail as possible, really immerse yourself into the scene.

When you can feel it and really be present with the experience, you will create emotion. The stronger the emotion, the higher the energy, and the higher the energy, the faster you will manifest your desires. When I was manifesting my book,

I would think about seeing it online, visualising people buying it all over the world and taking something positive from it, I would think about exactly what it looked like. I would also create even more emotion by thinking about how proud my children would be that Daddy has written a book, or how proud my parents would be to read my story. The more you can channel that inner emotion, the better.

Your subconscious mind doesn't know the difference between what's real and what's not, so if you manage to truly immerse yourself into the visualisation, and you feel as though you are experiencing that scene in real life, your mind is going to think it's happening in real life, and you are going to activate your reticular activating system (RAS). This is a group of neurons at the bottom of the brain that act as a filtering system and it's a seriously clever bit of kit. The RAS will filter out any information that is relevant to your vision and give it to you. You know like when you are looking to buy a red car and all of a sudden you see red cars everywhere? Or if you are expecting a baby, then all you see is pregnant people everywhere? That's your RAS system.

The more you visualise, the stronger your neural pathways will become in your brain and your mind will already think that you are living that life, then everything you desire will come to you rather than you trying to find it.

ACTION

- Plan in some time, maybe fifteen minutes where you can be alone in a comfortable environment and just imagine you have spent the next twenty years of your life being highly successful and achieving more success than you could have ever dreamt of. Think about where that would put you in twenty years' time, dream without limitations.
  - o What would you look like?
  - o What would you be wearing?
  - o Who would be with you?
  - o Where would you live?
  - o What would you eat?
  - o How many kids or grandkids would you have?
- Once you have the vision in mind, try and think about immersing your senses into the moment, what can you smell, taste and touch?
- This may take you some time to think of or it might come to you straight away, but you really want to make sure that it is you and it's the life you want to create, as this will become your destination.

GOAL SETTING – BETTER ME

A vision without a plan is just a dream.

My visualisation had sparked me into life; the more my limiting beliefs were falling away, the lighter I felt. It was as if the shackles of my past that had been weighing me down for so long were just dissolving around me, and I was able to focus my attention on the future. The vision was exciting and crystal clear, now I needed to translate it into a plan. Never one to over complicate things, I decided to keep the plan nice and simple, just become that future version of myself now. How he acts, what he looks like, what he eats, step by step I was just going to become him now.

The man in the blue shirt is slim and healthy, so I looked up what the ideal weight was on a BMI calculator and there it was, 30lb lighter than I was at the time. Prior to my understanding of the ego and how the mind works, I would have instantly thought of a million reasons why I couldn't hit that weight target. But now I could think without limitations, and I had a new positive mindset and felt as though there wasn't anything that I couldn't achieve, so I worked out that I would need to lose 30lb to get there. I gave myself six months to lose the weight, which made the goal seem far easier than I thought and off I went.

The man in the blue shirt eats a healthy Mediterranean-style diet, full of nutritious organic food that shines through in his healthy-looking hair and skin. So, I changed my diet and started to cut out processed foods and concentrated on organic whole foods instead. I started by setting myself the goal of eating a Mediterranean-style diet every day during the week and then allowing myself a cheat day at the weekend.

The man in the blue shirt is physically fit, and I was not, hence the need to lose 30lb. Thankfully, my recent lifestyle swap of alcohol for running meant that I had made a bit of progress, but I was far from fit. I decided to set myself some fitness goals. My first goal was 5km in twenty-six minutes, which was a stretch for me based on my condition at the time but was also achievable. Each month I set a goal of taking thirty seconds off my PB. The beautiful thing about fitness is that I had already noticed small improvements since I took up running and I knew that without the effects of alcohol every weekend, I would be able to make fairly quick progress.

The man in the blue shirt is surrounded by friends and family, which made me evaluate my relationships. They were all pretty weak, even with my immediate family. Years of suffering alone had caused me to isolate myself and try to get through it by myself, but now that my ego was no longer in the way, telling me that I was capable of doing it alone and I didn't need anyone else to help me, I was able to understand how important my family are in my life and how much I value them. Now was time to rebuild them stronger than ever before. I was very vocal to them all about the fact that I was working on completely rebranding myself as a new version that was focused on my family and that I valued each relationship individually. So, I set myself the goals of reaching out to my family and friends once a week and meeting up with my immediate family once a month.

I felt as though I was at a point in my life where I wanted to have some new friends, not because I didn't like my old friends, but because I was becoming a different person and I wanted to elevate myself. I wanted to surround myself with like-minded people and people who put health and fitness as well as relationships and sobriety at the top of their priority list. I set myself the goal of starting my own social media platform within the next six months, where I could share my journey to help other people, but also use it to build a community of my own, forming lots of new friendships in the process, so the Better Life Guy was born.

The one thing that was unclear about the man in the blue shirt was what he did for a living because he was retired. He had clearly had a successful life and appeared to radiate health and wellness, so I could guess that it was something to do with that, but I wasn't quite sure what. I had recently started to work on my book, and I felt a sense of purpose that I had never felt before, so I figured that if I kept on following that path of purpose then it would lead me into a new and exciting career. I gave myself one year to get the book written and published.

With goals set in all areas of my life, the transformation was on. All I needed to do was make sure I broke them all down and hit them at each and every checkpoint; nothing was going to stop me.

GOAL SETTING – BETTER YOU

O nce you have that vision in your mind of the life you are going to create, you need to create the goals that are going to get you there. Without setting goals, your life will simply pass you by and that's what happens to so many people. Goal setting is absolutely crucial to get from where you are now to where you want to be. Having a strong vision that you are emotionally attached to and then goals that will get you there, is the recipe for success. You will be pulled towards your vision like a paperclip to a magnet.

You have got to be as clear on the goals as you were on the vision. For example, if weight loss is your goal then you can't just say I want to lose weight, you need to know exactly what weight you want to be as well as when you aim to get there. If you say you want to lose weight without specifying exactly how much then you lose 2lb, you have achieved your goal, then what? You also want to practise visualising what you will feel like and how you will look when you get to the weight.

That is one of the most important tactics in hitting your goals, harnessing the power of emotion to pull you towards that end result.

Don't try and rush to get to your end goal. People overestimate what they can do in a week, but they underestimate what they can do in a year. Pretty much any goal is achievable if you allow yourself the time to build up to it; by giving yourself a good amount of time, it allows you to hit each milestone along the way, which will build confidence, giving you a much easier ride on the journey.

Get clear on your timescales, think about putting some incentives in along the way to motivate you to get to the next milestone. Think about when you are packing to go on holiday, you always get it done somehow right on time, or when you are moving to a new house and you think it's not possible to move so much crap in such a short time, but you do. That's because you have to, as there is a time limit attached. That's the mentality you need to assign to yourself when setting your goals.

Break down your goals into bitesize pieces and use the power of momentum to drive you forwards. Start as small as possible, especially if you are doing something that is outside of your comfort zone, as it can be daunting to begin with. For instance, if you have never done any running before, your first goal may be to get some running shoes on, go outside and do a five-minute walk just to get comfortable and tick off the first step, then build it up from there. but make sure you set yourself a goal to build up to, otherwise it will just fizzle out. Really small progress builds confidence and momentum, both key if you are going to successfully smash your goals.

Avoid the gold medal syndrome by always having your next goal in mind, especially when you are close to achieving the goal set in front of you. How many times do you see someone achieve a huge amount of weight loss and then they end up back where they started? Well, that's why you always have to keep your momentum going and continue to stretch your goal further.

Track your progression and reflect on your development. You will be amazed at how quickly you will progress in all areas of your life, but without keeping a track or record, you won't have any reference points to refer to. Use a running app to track your progress and store all of your records, look back through your bank statements to see how far your finances have come or take some pictures of yourself before starting that weight-loss journey. It may seem painful to do but this is the sort of motivation that money can't buy, and it will be a superpower when crushing your goals.

Celebrate success and reward yourself when you hit a goal. It's so important to take a minute to reflect and praise yourself when you have been working hard to hit a goal. We all love that feeling or achievement and acknowledgment, so when you smash your goal give yourself a little reward. Just don't hang around in the winner's circle for too long, as you can get too distracted and lose that well-earned momentum, onwards and upwards.

ACTION

- What does the future you look like?
- What do they do for a hobby?
- What does their diet consist of?
- What kind of weight are they?
- What clothes do they wear?
- Break down your goals into bitesize chunks, ensuring that they each one is very achievable.
- Make sure that your goals are sustainable and enjoyable so that they stand the test of time.
- Track your progress and make sure you celebrate your success at every milestone.

AFFIRMATIONS – BETTER ME

My ego was well on the way out, the vision of my future was clear in my mind, I had set myself specific goals that were going to propel me towards my vision, what else could I do to help myself on my journey? Affirmations.

The reason I decided to start using affirmations was because of all the learning I had done about the big, powerful subconscious mind. It's been set in its ways for ever and ever, and even though I had a plan in place and a vision to work towards, I knew that the subconscious mind would try its hardest to keep doing what it has always done and that is not helpful for me on my journey to becoming a new man.

Affirmations help to influence the subconscious mind that you are the person you want to become, so whilst I was already doing the things the man in the blue shirt would do, by using affirmations I would be able to help accelerate the rewiring process that needs to happen in the mind.

I started to explore the world of affirmations and wrote positive statements in the morning. I started to say them repeatedly over and over in my head: I am strong, I am successful, I am powerful. Using powerful words was intentional:

- "I am strong."
- "I am powerful."
- "I am replacing my bad habits with good habits."

I'm not going to lie, I found it quite strange at first and struggled to connect with the process. I would start laughing at myself quite often in the beginning. This was far from my normal routine. But like anything in life, the more I did it, the more it started to make sense, I could connect, and it became almost enjoyable. The hardest thing was saying them out loud. I live in a house of six people, so having the courage to start saying things like I am powerful and I am successful was all a bit weird to begin with, but after a while everyone just got used to it; they ignore me a lot of the time anyway!

I found it a lot easier to do outside, in the open air. It felt like I was connecting more with the universe too. I randomly started to shout them out after a run or whilst out on a walk, getting louder and louder the more confident I was getting with it. When the coast was clear, I would pause what I was listening to and start saying my affirmations out loud. It felt quite liberating, and much more powerful doing it out in the open air. I even started to plan a running route to finish a mile away from home so that I could walk back saying a load of positive affirmations out loud. I found that when I had finished running, I had serotonin flowing through my veins, which made the affirmations feel even more powerful.

I wrote a list of affirmations on the notes app on my phone and I would pull them up whenever I had a few minutes and just repeat them over and over again, sometimes whilst standing on the Tube, other times I would be walking down the road, even sitting on the toilet. Wherever I was, it didn't really matter, what mattered was that I was saying them, and I meant every word of each one. I found that if I was feeling weak in any way, my affirmations would give me strength and confidence, and if I was feeling confident, they would make me feel immortal. I never even knew what affirmations were before; now I was obsessed with them.

AFFIRMATIONS – BETTER YOU

The good news is that you will already be using affirmations in your daily life, you just don't know you are doing it. The bad news is that most people are using them to reaffirm negative thoughts about themselves.

If you are waking up every morning saying 'I am not good enough' then guess what, you have affirmed that belief to yourself and your mind will help you work towards it. The same goes for I am tired, or I am depressed. All you are doing is confirming your negative beliefs and strengthening that thought in your subconscious mind.

Now that you know what affirmations are and what they do, you can start to use them to assist you in hitting your goals rather than pulling you further away from them. By intentionally using positive affirmations, you help to reprogramme your subconscious mind, which in turn helps speed up the journey to a better you.

Your affirmations need to be very clear and strong and must be in the present tense, so start with 'I am…' They should be your affirmations and only be about you and your goals. Think about all of the parts of your life that you want to improve, write them down and say them out loud. If you want to start your own business but haven't got the confidence, you could use the affirmation, 'I am confident'. If you want to be successful but you don't think you deserve it, you could use, 'I am worthy of my success'.

You can say your affirmations at any point of the day, but first thing in the morning is a great place to start or just after you have practised gratitude. You can write the affirmations down on paper and read them in your own head, but the best way is to say them out loud. I like to say them after a run and when I'm out in the open air; it feels like I have a better connection to the universe when I'm high on serotonin. I get the odd funny look but who cares?

Another good method is to look in the mirror and say them out loud to yourself, looking yourself in the eye. No messing about there and that will tell you how much you believe them. The more you believe them the more they will push you in the right direction, but you must work with the thought, don't leave it hanging and hope it'll work out. If you say 'I am fit' but you don't start exercising, then it's not going to happen.

You must be consistent, and you must have faith; it's not a quick fix to reprogramme your mind, if it was then everyone would be doing it. Have fun, experiment with it, be patient, believe and the results will come.

ACTION

- Make sure that your affirmations are clear, strong and positive.
- They must be relevant to your goals.
- Say them out loud, ideally in front of a mirror or outdoors.
- Repeat them as often as you can.
- Always use the present tense, start with 'I am…'
- Believe in what you are saying.

JOURNAL – BETTER ME

When I was about ten years old, I had one of those diaries with a flimsy lock on the side and a key that came with it. I wrote my darkest secrets and most ambitious wishes into it for about three days before losing the key and then the diary itself. But there was something nice about doing it and the fact I can remember it tells me that it must have connected with me in some way.

The issue with journaling or using some form of diary is that it requires discipline, which is not something I have ever been particularly good at. I also used to despise the thought of having to do a specific task every day, it just didn't fit in with my lifestyle; I like to keep myself free and fluid. There were occasions where I thought to myself that I needed structure and I went and got myself a journal or a diary, but every single time it finished as quickly as it started. Because I didn't know what the benefits of journaling were and because I didn't get any tangible reward for doing it, I just wasn't interested.

It wasn't until my trip around the world that I picked up a journal and actually used it every day. This was the first time that I actually wrote in any form consistently over a long period of time and I absolutely loved it. Journaling whist travelling around the world is obviously a bit different to most forms of journaling; every day was filled with excitement about where I had been during that day or where I was heading next. I used to look forward to writing it at the end of each day and really liked the thought of having a record of everything I had done all in one place.

Returning from travelling with my journal all complete felt great, but I also knew that was the end of the trip therefore that was the end of my journaling. I had enjoyed the process so much that the thought crossed my mind to keep a journal going as I integrated back into reality, but the thought of recording what I did at work for the day unsurprisingly didn't fill me with the same level of excitement as it had when on my travels, so that was the end of that.

After hearing about the benefits of journaling during my personal development journey, it inspired me to dip my toe back into the water and see if it worked for me now that I was a bit more open to its benefits and a lot more mature to appreciate it. Initially I had the excitement of doing it, I felt as though it was a good thing to do, it almost felt like a secret weapon that not many people have in their locker, but as time went on, the momentum got lost and, as usual, it fizzled out. It wasn't until I gave up alcohol that I picked it back up and I started to journal properly and see the real benefit to it. Yet another benefit of the consistency that not drinking provides.

I read up on how to journal properly and I realised that the way I had been journaling previously was very much to look back and record rather than look forward and plan, probably because that was how I used it whilst traveling. Looking forwards was much more exciting, especially now that I had a vision to work towards. I started to get excited about writing it every morning, I made it enjoyable, I was more relaxed with the content and felt much more fluid. Some days I didn't want to write in it, so I didn't, and I was fine with it, it's a tool rather than a necessity. But the difference this time is that I picked it back up again and felt as though I had missed doing it when I had time off.

I started to use it in various ways; alongside the daily plotting and planning, I would pick it up if I was stuck on something, I would break it all down, write down why I felt stuck and just thrash it out with loads of notes, making a right mess of the page, but always getting an answer from doing it. I also used it for creativity. If I had an idea, I would just start to draw it or brainstorm it, and often it would lead me on a journey that I never would have predicted.

As my journaling evolved, I started to write down my daily affirmations as well as saying them out loud so that they had double the impact. Sometimes I would write out a page worth of them, other times I would write the same one over and over again, like I was back in detention writing lines. That's the beauty of journaling, you can just use it as you please.

Over time, I started to find a bit of rhythm with my journaling; first I would write down some things that I was grateful for, then I would go on to writing out my affirmations individually, then I started to combine all of my usual affirmations together into one power sentence. I would go on to record how I was feeling that day and what I wanted to achieve, and I would usually finish off by reminding myself what is important in my life and what I was working towards achieving.

I couldn't live without my journal now. I just love the process of doing it and I really feel the benefits of getting everything out of my head and onto paper. I love to see how it evolves week after week and I can't wait to see where I take it in the future.

JOURNAL – BETTER **YOU**

I f you have tried journaling before and didn't get on with it, then try it again, but this time with more of a forward-thinking approach. If you haven't tried it before then give it a go. Let's face it, a journal costs as much as a cup of coffee these days, so cost isn't an issue. It's a great way to make time for yourself, to gather your thoughts and make sure that you are aligned with what lies ahead, plus it's also fun when used correctly.

The best way to start journaling is to start journaling. It really is up to you what you want to write down, how often you want to look at it and how strict you are about using it. I found this to be the best way to start. Just put a few notes in it to begin with and start to use it consistently, then it will evolve in a very short space of time, and before you know it, you will have filled the thing up and be buying the next one.

I'm not generally someone who looks backwards in life, but on the odd occasion it's nice to reflect and see how far I have come on my journey. You can also use it to see if there are any patterns that emerge that you may not be aware of. For example, you may be more creative on a Thursday, more frustrated on Mondays or grateful on a Sunday. Having an awareness of any mood patterns will give you an advantage when you are planning when to do certain tasks or work.

Journaling is a great way to ensure that you stick to your goals; by writing them down and holding yourself accountable, you are far more likely to achieve them. It is also a great way to start trying something new. For example, you may want to write down three things you are grateful for in the morning, you may want to set yourself a challenge for the day, you could even use it to help plan what you will eat. Once it's complete, you will feel a sense of achievement and set yourself up for a much more productive day than ever.

It's a fantastic tool to have as a security blanket because it's always there and it should be your first stop whenever you are stuck, confused or frustrated, as it allows you the freedom to write or draw whatever you want, which then minimises the risk of you actually saying anything that you might regret. It's also a creator's paradise; you have the freedom to do what you want, probe your own ideas, be adventurous with your thoughts and remember that thoughts become things.

You can do what you want with your journal. Remove any previous judgments you had about journaling and just see it for what it is, an empty book. Draw on it, take your frustrations out in it, check in with yourself from time to time in it, but most of all make sure that it's enjoyable – never feel like you have to do it, feel like you want to do it.

ACTION

- Purchase a journal, either a notepad or something that's more structured. *The Better Life Journal* by Dean Graziosi is my personal favourite.
- Make sure that you are relaxed when journaling.
- Keep your entry fluid: an easy structure is to reflect on what happened yesterday, what you are grateful for in the present and what you are planning for the future.
- Try and use it every day. You will find it becomes much easier as you get used to it.
- Make sure you are in a relaxed environment as you write.
- Finish with a strong positive message to yourself or affirmations.
- Read your entry when you finish.

ADAPT

"If you always do what you've always done, you'll always get what you've always got."

Henry Ford

Now that you understand the way we work as humans and the power of the mind, and you are starting to visualise your exciting new future, it's time to start implementing some changes.

Remember, if you change nothing, nothing changes.

REVIEW YOUR CREW — BETTER ME

I have always been someone who likes to be amongst it, with plenty of friends in plenty of different places. Friends always have and always will play a big part in my life, but as with everything in life, they come and go. There are only a few people I would class as lifelong friends and fortunately I have known them since I was five years old; we have grown up together and have always been there for each other at times of celebration and desperation.

Growing up, I always had different groups of friends; football friends, school friends, those friends that you know you shouldn't be hanging around with friends. Girls, boys, older, younger, it didn't really bother me, I just liked being with people and making new friends. The friends I always attract are usually similar to myself, confident, adventurous and downright hilarious. When I started working in retail, I found the industry to be full of amazing people that had a bit about them, took pride in their appearance and were always good for a laugh, which was one of the many reasons that I loved going to work every day.

Working in the fashion industry in central London gave me some of the closest friendships I've ever had. Colleagues that I spent all day with became friends that I would spend the evenings with. Working with such a talented group of people and building such amazing friendships along the way gave me some of the best memories of my life and immersing myself into my job and the team I created made for an extremely successful combination. But drinking was the glue that held the group together and being amongst it all in the bright lights of the West End was one of the biggest reasons I got into it in the first place, so going sober was obviously going to have an effect on the people who I was spending time with and the places that I was hanging out.

I loved all my friends dearly, they were great people, but by making such fundamental changes to my lifestyle, the people I spent the most time with were the people who were in the places that I no longer wanted to hang out, in the bars and pubs. I had to make the changes for me, I had to make sure that my friends were in line with my future. It wasn't that I wanted to remove people from my friendship circle, I wanted to add people to it, people who were going to elevate me personally and professionally.

To my surprise, most of my friendships didn't really diminish, they just adapted and became more grown up and mature.

I had been so worried that I was going to lose my closest friends that I had been stressed out about that more than making the actual changes themselves. Some of my closest friends even came out and said that they were glad I had stopped drinking as they didn't want to continue with the boozy lifestyle anymore, but they didn't want to be the one to say it. I was so relieved and happy that everyone was so supportive of my life-changing decisions, and glad to have kept hold of those people that have been a big part of my journey. Now I could look forwards and focus on who I wanted to bring into my life next.

I was evolving into a different person more and more each day. I had been watching a lot of Jim Rohn videos on YouTube; he is one of the best motivational speakers ever to have lived and I just loved everything he said. One of the things that stuck with me the most was when I heard him say, "You are the average of the five people you spend the most time with." I looked back at the person I had been over the years, and I could see that it was true. I wanted to use that knowledge to cherry-pick who I was going to spend the most time with in the next chapter of my life.

At this particular point in time, the world was in lockdown as the coronavirus pandemic had just kicked off, so I wasn't spending time with anyone other than my family. Having that time away from the world and being in the process of remodelling myself provided me with some time to think about who I was going to bring into my friendship group and how that would even be possible. It's not like you can go out and find five successful people, knock on their door and ask if you can be their friend, but I was talking to people online more than ever and I was really enjoying building friendships through social media. And, let's be honest, most people these days spend more time talking to their friends online than they do in person anyway, so it appeared to be the way to go.

The months went by, and I was talking to lots of people online, mainly other people who had gone sober, but also people that were into personal development and the power of the mind. I had started to build a little network of people who I looked forward to hearing from or enjoyed watching what they were up to each day on their social media. It was all really helping me to move forward in my own journey. Then when I had the idea of creating my own social media account dedicated just to like-minded people it all clicked. I could create my own community of people and build a team of people who are all on the same journey. I visualised what it would look like, then how it would feel to meet up with everyone or even hold events as a group.

The excitement was real, I could have friends all over the world, from all different backgrounds and cultures. I could learn so much, but also inspire people myself. By maintaining my old friendships and building new ones online, I was able to have the perfect blend of people to supplement my new lifestyle and set me up for success.

REVIEW YOUR CREW – BETTER YOU

So going by what Jim Rohn said, if you hang around with five smokers, you'll be the sixth, if you hang around with five drug takers, you'll be the sixth, if you hang around with five drinkers, you'll be the sixth. But that same principle also works in a positive way too. If you want to start eating more vegan food, then start spending time with more vegan people, either online or in real life. The same goes for any healthy habit you want to pick up: if you want to start running, join a running club, that's a great way to meet new friends who share the same passion.

The question to ask yourself is, are the people you spend the most time with helping you achieve your newly created vision? If the answer is no, then that's okay. It doesn't mean that you need to lose that person out of your life, it just means you need to spend less time with them and spend more time with the people who will help you on your way.

Do you have those people close to you who have a strong association with some of your unhealthy habits? Maybe you have a lifelong friend that you feel you should meet up with but every time you do it ends up in the pub and you are chatting shit for three hours, but have you ticked a box? Well, now it's time to mix it up. Why not suggest meeting for breakfast rather than dinner, or going for a walk and talk rather than a wine and whine. Remember that your friend may well join you on your new journey and you may be the one to inspire them into a new healthier lifestyle.

The thing is that if you are serious about becoming a better you then you need to change what you've always done. Now I'm not suggesting you go and throw away years of friendships and go get a table for one, I am simply asking you to review your crew. Are they people who will help you on your journey or will they hold you back? Can you adapt the environment in which you meet them? Can you spend less time with the people who will hold you back and more time with the people who will help you grow?

Friends are friends, they come and they go, but real friends will stay, no matter what happens they will stick by you and support you, especially when you are making such positive changes to your own life. Anyone who doesn't isn't worth keeping in the first place.

ACTION

- Write down who your closest friends are and decide if they are going to be the people who will support you in your new life.
- Some of them may be fine, but you may need to reduce the time you spend with anyone who isn't going to be supportive. (Note – you may be surprised who wants to join you on the journey, especially once you start bursting with energy and enthusiasm, so it's worth giving everyone a shot.)
- Who do you want to spend more time with? These people should elevate you, so be brave and aim high.
- Make sure that you adjust your social media following accordingly. Stop looking at all the people who are constantly glamourising being drunk and start following people who will inspire you to reach your goals.

COMFORT ZONE – BETTER ME

I was always pretty good at pushing myself out of my comfort zone. I moved out on my own at seventeen years old, took myself around the world for a year at the age of twenty-three, moved to London alone at twenty-four, I was always on the lookout for a new job role, or new place to live, a different city to explore. But I wasn't aware that I was doing it, it just felt pretty normal to me. But, as the years go on and the pressures of life build, I found myself inside my comfort zone more and more.

Not dealing with the grief of losing Rocco had put a big dent in my confidence and halted my ambition for life. It also led to me reaching for the lazy coping mechanisms of alcohol and drugs. Each day was another day to tick off that was moving me further away from the event in the hope that would bring relief. I had gone from thriving with new challenges and loving exploring different places, to wanting to do the complete opposite, staying in my comfort zone, which consisted of the pub, a bar or my sofa. I was stuck in this trap, unsure how to move on and living one day to the next, just about getting by.

By being in my comfort zone for so many years, everything that was previously free-flowing was now left to stagnate. All my creativity was drying up as I found myself drinking more, eating more and generally punishing my body. I became more and more frustrated at the lack of progression in my life, but also knew that I was the one causing it. I would flirt with the idea of giving up drinking and starting over, but the pull was too strong, and the comfort zone always won. It wasn't until I lost it all that things started to change.

It was that visit from the man outside the bar that sparked me back into action; when he told me that I was going to live until I was ninety-seven and I was going to be very successful, I had a bit of a wake-up call. I thought to myself, 'Yeah, I am going to be fucking successful. I have a lot to offer this world, what am I doing wasting my time drinking, rooted in my comfort zone? I am better than this.' I was back in the game and my journey of recovery had begun.

Once I started listening to the podcasts on mindset, I kept hearing about the importance of stepping out of your comfort zone. The quote I always remember hearing was your comfort zone is where your dreams go to die, and I knew exactly how that felt. I remembered what an ambitious man I am and was annoyed that I had wasted so much time stuck, not creating, not exploring, and not meeting new people. I was on a mission to make up for lost time.

Stepping out of my comfort zone became a bit of a game and was quite addictive. I started with the smallest of changes and built them up day by day. I would go and speak to a stranger or make conversation with someone at work who I wouldn't normally speak to. I would set a target to pay a set number of people a compliment each day. I got off the Tube at different stops and walked a different route to work. I would eat something for lunch I had never tried before. I learnt a new word and tried to get it into as many conversations as possible. It all sounds a bit weird, but it was working, I felt amazing.

Now that I was aware of what I was doing, I could see how so many other people were living locked inside their comfort zone and it motivated me to want to help other people smash through it and into the world of adventure and opportunity. That was what led to me having the idea of sharing my journey and what better way for a man who didn't do well at school than to write and publish a book.

Even for a confident person like me, writing a book was way out of my comfort zone. I didn't do well at school, I can't spell very well, and my handwriting is atrocious. I also knew that the book needed to contain the full details of my personal life to give it the context it needed to be successful, so that was another big step outside of my comfort zone. I hadn't even discussed this with my closest family members before, now I planned on telling the world.

Now I constantly do things that are outside my comfort zone, have made sure that if I am feeling too comfortable at anything in my life, I review it and move it on. Don't get me wrong, I still like sitting on my sofa watching the football on Sunday afternoon, that's pretty comfortable! But I'm talking about the job that becomes mundane, or the gym class that becomes easy, the relationship that starts to feel too comfortable, that's when it's time to step it up a gear and keep progressing.

COMFORT ZONE – BETTER YOU

You have got your vision, you know where you want to go, and you know where you are now with the comfort bubble that exists around you. Now grab a pin and pop that motherfucker. I'm going to use this quote again:

> "If you always do what you've always done, you'll always get what you've always got."

Success lies on the other side of fear, and you know that by living your life in the bubble of your comfort zone, you are going to be able to predict your future, which by the way will be safe, unfulfilled and boring. So, if you are serious about living a life you have never lived before, you must start doing things you have never done.

There have been many studies that have investigated what people regret in their lives and the biggest regret is not going for that goal, not taking that risk and not seeing what they could do with their life. If you imagine yourself on your deathbed at the end of your life and look back at the life you have lived, are you going to have those same regrets? Most people will because they are living in fear, fear of what other people will think, fear that they aren't good enough. Feel the fear and do it anyway. Use that motivation to push you out of your comfort zone and see what you can do with your life.

Life isn't made to sip cocktails on a beach, you are supposed to grow and progress and to do that you need to keep pushing yourself outside your comfort zone. Stop wasting all that time binging the next Netflix season, playing the PlayStation or moaning on Facebook. Challenge yourself to be different, try new things and don't be afraid to fail, visit new places, enjoy getting lost, talk to new people, try new food, whatever you do, do not stay still. Think about what happens to water if it stops flowing. It becomes stagnated and mouldy. Do you want to be a smelly pond or a fresh stream?

ACTION

- Spend a few minutes reflecting on the last time you stepped outside your comfort zone, when was it and how did you feel afterwards?
- How can you make small changes to start to break free from your comfort zone? Maybe it's trying something new to eat or taking a different route to work or starting a conversation with someone who you have never spoken to before.
- Challenge yourself physically and mentally.
- Write down what you plan on doing to break free from your comfort zone today and make it happen.
- As you get more confident, start to challenge yourself to face your fears.
- Start a new hobby or join a local club.
- Be kind to yourself, use this as an opportunity to incorporate some more positivity into your life or the life of others.

ENVIRONMENT – BETTER ME

had always lived in a nice house and worked for amazing brands that inspired me, so I thought I was well covered when it came to the environment that I spent most of my time in. But what I wasn't aware of is that my environment was far more than just the place I lived or worked in, it was what I was watching, what I was listening to and the places where I was hanging out. All of it makes up the environment and it all plays a part in your level of success, or not as the case was for me.

My own working space has always been pretty clean and tidy as I hate working in a mess, so there wasn't too much to change there. One of the first real changes I made to my environment was to the music I was listening to. I had never paid attention to what the lyrics to the songs I was listening to were saying, I had been singing out loud to songs that were actually saying some pretty disturbing things. Now that I was familiar with the power of words and was utilising them through my daily affirmations, I could see how damaging some of my music choices had been to my success in life.

It was the same story when it came to what I was watching. It never occurred to me that I was watching things that were influencing the way I think, therefore affecting who I am. The examples that sprung to mind immediately weren't from what I was watching on TV, but what I was watching online and in particular on social media. Whether it was reading through the comments on the latest political disaster or watching a pair of school mums having it out on Facebook, I was wasting my time and it was affecting me in a negative way – you could say it was a lose-lose.

Not only did I immediately stop myself from having these negative influences in my life, but I saw an opportunity to hack my environment and use my environment to my advantage. I started listening to motivational music with positive lyrics in the morning, screaming out songs like 'Happy' by Pharrell Williams in the shower every morning. I went on a mission to delete any negative people off my social media, and I replaced them with positive people and influencers from the world of sobriety and personal development. I stopped reading the paper and started to carry a book around with me to read instead. I stopped watching the news and started to watch things that I was interested in learning about, like documentaries or educational YouTube videos.

I even took it to the next level and had some prints made that had positive messages on and had them framed all around the house. This was so they were absorbed into my subconscious mind, but also they would be absorbed by everyone in the family too. They said things like, 'positive mind positive life' or 'have courage and be kind' or, 'you totally can'. I loved it, they made an impact on me straight away and I would find myself looking for them throughout the day.

I had managed to completely flip my negative environment having a negative effect on my life into a positive environment having a positive effect on my life. I won't let anything slip back to how it was in any part of my life. My environment now sets me up for success.

ENVIRONMENT – BETTER YOU

We have already covered being inspired by your vision and the people around you, but are you inspired by your environment? If not, why not?

Think about how much of a difference it would make to your life if you were inspired every day by where you live or work. Let's face it, the sad fact is that most people spend more time with their work colleagues in their work environment than they do with their own family. So, if the environment where you spend most time is not inspiring you to perform at your best then guess what? You've got to change it.

If you are serious about becoming a better you, then it's time to level up and there are plenty of levels to go to here. I'm not suggesting you quit your job and move home (although I wouldn't rule it out), but I am suggesting you look into what changes you can make aesthetically. It might be as simple as a lick of paint, some flowers, some candles or room scents, changing the radio station, making sure it's the right temperature. These are all fairly basic changes that can make a big difference to your personal performance.

If these changes aren't going to work then don't be afraid to make bigger ones, following the pandemic, it is now much more acceptable to work from home. If so, then can you get a space at home that you can make look and feel like you need it to in order to maximise your potential? Can you work outside? Is there another part of the building you can move to? Don't be afraid to ask the questions or make the changes, these may be for the benefit of everyone, and everyone might be pleased to listen to your suggestions.

Another common problem with environment is mess. If you have a ton of paperwork all over your desk, you are far less likely to be motivated to deliver a piece of excellent work. If your bedroom has clothes and shoes everywhere then you are much less likely to feel relaxed and sleep well. Even the way in which you organise the desktop of your computer or the home screen of your phone will affect you and your performance.

You are what you consume. If you spend your time scrolling through Facebook all day, you'll probably start to become one of those people who ends up complaining or moaning about something all the time. If you are always watching the news, you will probably become more anxious and worried about life and all the problems we supposedly face. If you watch a lot of reality TV, you will automatically focus more on shallow, superficial parts of your life and drive home any insecurities you have within yourself. This goes for all the music you listen to; if you are singing along to some kind of morbid love song, that's going to make you upset and bring you down.

Don't let your own environment hold you back from achieving greatness. You are in control of what you consume, use that power wisely.

ACTION

- What does your environment look like? Particularly in the places you spend the most time (work, home, bedroom).
- What can you do to upgrade the environment in these spaces?
- What's the lighting like? What does it smell like?
- Who are you following on social media? Are they motivating you or are they lowering your vibration?
- What are you watching on TV? Is it helping to inspire you into becoming a better you?
- What music are you listening to? What are the lyrics saying that are soaking into your ears?
- Start to replace negative followers, music taste or TV shows with inspiring, positive people and content, and watch what happens to your mood.

HABITS – BETTER **ME**

had always associated habits as being bad behaviours that I had picked up over the course of my life and now formed part of who I am today. Things like biting my nails or jigging my leg repeatedly to more serious habits like drinking alcohol or taking drugs were all habits that I had picked up. But now that I had a vision of who I wanted to be in the future, it made me think differently about my habits and it gave me someone to compare myself with. The man in the blue shirt lives a life of health and fitness, eating nutritious food and spending most of his time outside in the beautiful Spanish sunshine. He isn't sitting there getting drunk and biting his nails.

One thing I had never really considered was how I could create my own habits to support me on my way to becoming my best self. I read a variety of books that talked about the importance of habits and how they act as building blocks when creating a new self. This made perfect sense; by consciously forming new habits and incorporating them into my lifestyle I could effectively design my life. All I had to do was show up every day and do what needed to be done.

I learned that by creating habits for myself, it would have another big benefit, I wouldn't be draining my willpower throughout the day because a habit just happens, I don't have to think about it, it's just what I do at that time of the day, meaning there are no internal arguments over whether or not I can be bothered to do it, I have no choice in the matter. That means that for the rest of the day I have a full bar of willpower, which means that I am far less likely to give into any sort of temptation.

I started to play a game of trade with my old habits and behaviours with the new ones I needed to become the man in the blue shirt. He doesn't drink so I'll stop drinking, he eats lots of nutritious, whole food, so I'll do that, he is fit and healthy, so I'll carry on running and join a gym, he sleeps well every night and gets up early every morning, I can do that. Before I knew it, I was halfway there, I just needed to keep doing it so that the behaviour became a habit.

I started to build a routine to reflect my new vision. I decided that I would go for a run every Tuesday, Thursday and Saturday. This was non-negotiable and would happen regardless of weather or circumstances. If I had a meeting early in the morning I would run even earlier, if I was going away for the night, I'd take my running gear with me. If I run for thirty minutes on a Tuesday and Thursday, then an hour on a Saturday, that's two hours per week out of 168 hours that we are given, that's not much. It's still giving me four days per week of NOT running.

I wanted to try the early morning thing but wasn't really sure what the purpose of it was. Then someone recommended a book to me called *The Miracle Morning* by Hal Elrod. That book changed the game for me and provided me with much-needed structure for my early morning routine. I started to get up at 5am every day and get a head start on life, allocating a set amount of time to sit in silence to visualise my new life, write down affirmations, gratitude and journal, and do some form of exercise, which was different depending on the day. If it was a non-running day I would do a home workout, or some sit ups; it wasn't a lot of exercise that was needed, it was just about setting the day up the best way possible.

I started to eat a Mediterranean-style diet every single day, focusing on nutrition and eating good quality whole foods. This made me feel incredible! Bizarrely, I had never looked at food as something that can make you feel good, I've always focused on the food you should avoid that make you gain weight, not foods you should enjoy that give you energy.

I started looking at upgrading the habits I already did; I brushed my teeth every day but rarely flossed, so I made sure that I did both every day. I even looked at my shower routine and transformed it from something that I just got in and did to something that had a routine. I went and invested in nicer body wash, face scrubs and shampoo that made me enjoy the process much more than doing it because I had to. I then felt nice and fresh when I got out and I wasn't just focusing on getting to my next task.

One of the best things I discovered whilst learning about habits was something called habit stacking. What a game changer that is. Habit stacking is exactly what you think it is, it's when you intentionally stack your habits together, two for the price of one, if you like. What an amazing idea, I could use a habit that I knew I would do to trigger myself into doing something I was more likely to forget doing. The first thing I started with was supplements. I had been to the health store and got myself a load of different supplements to take every day in order to maximise my health, but I kept forgetting to take them. So, I left them in a pot that was near the dishwasher so that every time I put my dinner plate in the dishwasher, I would see them and take them. The act of putting the plate in the dishwasher was my trigger to take my supplements. Habit stacking worked well for me, so I started to take it a bit further by adding another layer. I would use the act of taking my supplements as the trigger to make me go for a short walk. Dinner, supplements, walk. Every day. My habits were little building blocks that were driving me towards my goals with minimal effort, what a life hack.

HABITS – BETTER YOU

A habit is behaviour that is repeated over and over again until it becomes automatic. Once it becomes automatic, you know that it is ingrained in your subconscious mind and it's just a part of who you are and what you do. The beautiful thing about habits is that you can create them and hack your own mind. Think about it, habits can be amazing tools for us to use if we create the right ones. If you go for a walk at 6am every day, and meditate at 6pm every day, and perform a skin care ritual before you go to bed every single day, then over a period of months, all of these tasks will become habits and, once they become habits, they become automatic. You can literally programme yourself to become an automatically run superhuman.

Creating habits also stops you from using up your willpower bar. Think of it like a computer game where you wake up with a full bar of willpower and, as the day goes on, you lose a bit at a time. For example, if you are debating with yourself over whether or not you should go for a run today as it's cold and raining, but you know you should, so you either go for a half-hearted run or you don't even go, either way you have drained the life out of that willpower supply.

By programming into your life-specific habits, they will become things that you do without the need to negotiate with yourself, therefore you won't need to touch your willpower level. The thing with the willpower bar is that the lower it gets the more likely you are to make stupid decisions or say something you shouldn't or reach for the cookie jar before bed.

Write a list of all of the habits that you want to create and see where you can fit them into your routine. For example, I run every Tuesday, Thursday and Saturday as that is what works best for me with the kids' school routine and it's also an achievable habit that never has to be questioned or adapted. I meditate at 7pm every night when the kids are in bed, and I know that I can commit to it without fail. Obviously, you will need to try different times and adjust accordingly, but just take it easy and do it when it feels right.

Ideally you should aim to load as many of your high priority habits at the start of your day as possible because you will be fully refreshed in the morning and more likely to enjoy them as well as doing them properly.

Write them all down, plot them into your schedule and just turn up and do them, it's that simple. Remember it's going to take a few weeks to plunge them into your subconscious, so you are going to need to be consistent and work hard and it will pay you back big time later on in the journey to becoming the better you.

It is equally as important to consider what habits you have that don't fit in with your new better life.

Breaking a bad habit isn't very easy, but it is doable. There are a couple of things to consider when attempting to stop doing something. Remember when we talked about new neural connections in the brain being formed when you do something new? And how the more you do something the stronger these connections are? Well, that is why it's so difficult to stop something you have been doing for so long, it's a process of building the new pathways and dissolving the old ones, so it will take time.

Try replacing your bad habit with a new one. This was a great recommendation that I had, and it led to me swapping drinking for running. Every time I wanted a drink, I would go and run it off. That worked so well for me and gave me the feel-good hormones at the same time.

Hold yourself accountable for your habits, you are an adult, and you are in control. Don't allow yourself to slip back into your old habits. If you slip up, get straight back onto the task and try to learn what triggered the mistake.

Remember why you are doing it in the first place and use your visualisation to pull you forward to the end goal and your better life.

ACTION

- What habits do you have that no longer serve you? Write them down and get to work on stopping them one at a time.
- What habits do you want to build into your new lifestyle? These could be exercise, nutrition, mindset or spiritual.
- What does your morning routine look like? Could you wake up earlier every day and build some helpful habits into your morning routine?
- What does your personal care routine look like? Can you upgrade the products you use and the quality of care you give yourself?
- Remember that once you commit to a behaviour over and over again, it becomes a habit, once it's a habit it is programmed into your subconscious as an automatic behaviour. This will require minimal willpower to achieve, leaving you with more energy and less risk for the rest of the day.

PHYSICAL

"It is health that is real wealth and not pieces of gold and silver."

Mahatma Gandhi

ALCOHOL – BETTER ME

As a kid growing up, one of my fondest memories was when we would have friends and relatives over to our house for a BBQ in summer. I vividly remember watching my parents and their friends all seemingly having so much fun, laughing all day long and not having a care in the world. When I arrived at that point in my life, it felt like a bit of a letdown. The summer BBQs were something I was looking forward to doing with my friends and family, but they weren't as fun in reality as they were from the eyes of a young boy. You are constantly topping people's drinks up, it costs a fortune to host and the longer it goes on, the louder everyone becomes.

The association I had with alcohol growing up was that it was something that all adults do, it's fun and I couldn't wait to be able to drink it myself. Whereas when I started drinking myself, I realised that the reality is very different. I went through the same experience most teenagers do of drinking in the park with mates, pretending to enjoy the taste of a warm can of lager, pretending not to be drunk when having a couple of drinks with the family, whilst in reality my head was all over the place. These years were about finding out my tolerance levels. Unfortunately that was quite a painful adventure, leading to some awkward situations, some painful apologies and some embarrassing mistakes, but hey that's just what you do at that age, right?

Through my twenties I wouldn't really drink from Monday to Thursday, but then I would hammer it over the weekend. I wouldn't even say I really enjoyed the taste of it, but it was fun, and it was what everyone else did. It gave me confidence within a social environment, provided entertainment at house parties and I got off pretty lightly on the hangover front.

But in my late twenties, things started to change. Drinking had gone from something I did for fun into something I was becoming more reliant on. I was using alcohol more and more as a coping mechanism when dealing with the general stresses of life. I had a better job, leading to more responsibility, I started earning more money and bought my first house, I financed a nice car and had become a father for the first time. This all happened pretty quickly, and I am not sure I was ready to deal with it.

My drinking habits grew alongside my responsibilities and, as it crept up, I really started to feel the physical effects of drinking. Heartburn was my arch enemy; I would get away with it earlier on in the week when I was being a bit more sensible, I would usually get away with it until Friday night, but then it would kick the shit out of me all weekend and I would be eating Gaviscon like sweets trying to fend it off. I even had to adapt my choice of drink to whatever would give me the least reaction to heartburn. I also started to break out in blotches of dry skin as the dehydration kicked in, which led to me carrying around a bottle of moisturiser with me everywhere I went. Although I knew exactly why I was getting these ailments, I never thought about cutting down my drinking, that just wasn't an option, I would rather find a remedy than a cure.

Rocco died three weeks before my thirtieth birthday. Following his death, my relationship with alcohol went from a want to a need overnight. For all of my adult life I had seen people use alcohol as a coping mechanism for dealing with stress and grief, not only friends and family but it's in the movies and every TV show I'd ever seen. It was all I knew, and it was all I had.

I drank every single day for well over a year, partly to numb the pain, partly to escape reality and partly to harm myself. Alcohol is the world's biggest fraudster. I thought it was taking away the pain but in fact it was suppressing it and letting it build up slowly and even multiply. I was also conned into thinking that alcohol would help me sleep, but whilst it gave me the initial knockout blow, it also guaranteed my sleep quality was absolutely terrible and I would be lying in bed staring at the ceiling feeling highly emotional, physically terrible and mentally exhausted, but hey it sent me off to sleep so I figured that is better than not being able to fall asleep at all.

I got to the point where my body started to hurt so much that I would have to take a break from drinking, only for a couple of days, just long enough to feel better. As hard as it was to have these intermittent breaks, I felt much better in myself and for the first time I started to realise that drinking alcohol was not helping me in any way. Even having a few days off it, I would sleep better, my diet would improve, and I would just feel a bit clearer in my mind. But despite feeling so much better physically and mentally, I was always pulled back to the drink because of the instant hit of relaxation that I got. I was taking the short-term gain, long-term pain route, but it seemed a lot easier than dealing with real life at the time and I couldn't contemplate facing the world without it.

The more I was drinking, the higher my tolerance became, so I started to look for harder options. Beer drinking changed to spirits, I started to take drugs as often as I could, cocaine ideally but I would take anything that I could get my hands on. I started smoking and basically spiralling out of control. With the addition of cocaine in my life I was able to go for longer, so the drinking days turned into drinking weekends, leading to me feeling awful by the time Monday came around. Alcohol had led my down a path of self-destruction and I hit rock bottom with a pretty hard bang. Losing my marriage, my family home and nearly my own life was a pretty rough ride, but not as rough as losing my boy, and that was what I still hadn't dealt with.

When I met Kirsty, we instantly had a connection, and it was as though the universe had sent her to me as a gift. We would spend hours sitting up at night talking and for the first time I was letting everything out and it felt amazing. The more I was talking to her, the lighter I felt emotionally and the less I was becoming so reliant on alcohol. My drinking sessions in London slowed down as I spent more and more time with Kirsty. I couldn't wait to get home and get talking, and we would share a bottle of wine over dinner rather than having eight beers and a line. With every day I was feeling better, I started to feel a spring in my step and after a while my breaks from alcohol started to be weeks rather than days.

I started to challenge myself to see if I could go for two weeks, three weeks or even a month without alcohol and, when I achieved it, I felt better than I had done for years. Any ailments, internal aches and pains just went. My eyes were brighter, and my skin started to glow. I was crushing it at work. I had also started my personal development journey, which motivated me more and more to live with purpose and passion and gave me a real sense of direction, something I had been lacking for some time. I started to fantasise about what life would be like if I felt like this every day.

Now I was looking at alcohol differently, my relationship started to change and I became more and more conscious of the effects it was having on my body. I started to analyse how I felt whilst drinking, the day after drinking, how it affects my sleep quality, what I was eating as a result, what my concentration levels were like the day after, how it affected my personality and behaviour before, during and after drinking. It all started to become very clear, my eyes were now open, I was aware for the first time in my life, and I was shocked at what I had been doing to myself for all these years.

My newfound awareness caused me to look at everyone differently. I could see who was controlled by alcohol and who wasn't, I watched people's behaviour change as soon as they started drinking. I was fascinated by it and couldn't help but think of how I had previously behaved and what a dickhead I must have looked, but also so grateful that I was now aware of it and wanting to change.

I knew that I needed to find some new friends who would inspire me to drink less or not drink at all, so I started to look for inspiration online and I found a guy called Andy Ramage. I saw him on the Rich Roll podcast, and I thought I would just watch it for a few minutes on my phone. Over an hour and a half later, I had watched the whole thing in amazement. He was working in a sociable, boozy culture in London, so was I, he was into his health and fitness but then lost his way and drank too much, same as me, he was a guy who was full of ambition but holding himself back because of his own drinking problem, that was me too. Since going sober, every part of his life has significantly improved, you could see the spark in his eye and, for the first time in my life, I was considering doing the unthinkable and going sober too.

I found an online sober community that was full of regular people like me who all had a story to tell, but they were a different breed to the people I was used to. They weren't looking backwards and dwelling on the past, they were focused on where they are today and where they are going in their future. They were creators, inspirational motivators, supporters of one and other, accountable for their behaviour and ambition. I had spent my life thinking that I was one of those people but in fact I was living for the weekends and working hard for the pay cheque. These people love life every day, whether it's a Monday or a Saturday it doesn't matter, because without the influence and control of alcohol you get so much back from life and you fall back in love with being yourself. I wanted a piece of that pie.

The RAS system kicked in and I started to notice alcohol-free drinks in every bar and every supermarket, I couldn't believe the selection that was available, I had thought there was only one 0% beer on the market. I even noticed people that were drinking 0% beers in bars and pubs around London. I would have laughed at people drinking that before, or probably not even noticed them as I was too focused on getting my next drink, but now I was intrigued. I even went and talked to a few people and bombarded them with questions about why they weren't drinking, do they ever drink, what's it like not drinking, what are 0% beers like. My view on sobriety had gone from one that thought it was ridiculous to one that I was now gripped by.

Seeing how far the alcohol-free drinks world was moving, I was excited to go and give them a try. I opted to do this in the privacy of my own home as I wasn't brave enough to do it in public. They tasted amazing; I could barely tell the difference in some of them. I was so surprised how good they were that it gave me even more of a feeling that I was drifting towards a life of sobriety. Good quality alcohol-free drinks meant that I could still have the thought and excitement of looking forward to a beer, I could get a cold beer out of the fridge or from the bar and enjoy that initial feeling, but afterwards I could go to the gym or out for a run rather than carry on drinking into the night. I could go home for a salad rather than order a pizza, I could have a good night's sleep rather than waking up thirsty and hungover. It all made so much more sense.

With all of this knowledge now circling in my mind, I knew it was something I wanted to do, but it was going to take a very brave decision to actually go through with it, let alone announcing it to my friends and family. Being someone who worked in the fashion industry in central London and would be at every event going, the social pressure of things was a real concern for me. How would everyone react to me not drinking? Would I be able to actually go out and socialise with my friends and watch them get drunk? Would people still want to know me? These were all very big questions in my mind, and I wasn't sure how it would go.

After a stint of a few weeks not drinking, I decided to write down all the benefits of drinking on one side of paper and all the benefits of sobriety on the other and the results were pretty one sided:

BENEFITS OF NOT DRINKING:

1. I look better.
2. I feel much better.
3. I have more energy.
4. I can think clearly.
5. My focus is much better.
6. I am eating healthier.
7. I am seeing progression in my fitness.
8. I am sleeping much better.
9. I am a better father / partner / friend.
10. I am less anxious.
11. My ailments virtually disappear.
12. I am losing weight.
13. My performance at work is better.
14. My hair and skin feel better.

BENEFITS OF DRINKING:

1. More fun.
2. Something to look forward to.
3. Better social life.
4. I like the taste.
5. I like how it makes me feel.

The benefits of sobriety were facts, whereas the benefits of drinking were questionable. More fun? Really? Is it more fun to sit down drinking than having meaningful experiences, conversations with the people that really matter in your life? Is it really more fun to let go of your inhibitions and regret various conversations and actions? Is it fun to waste that time and money I could be spending with my family? Is it fun to feel like shit and waste thousands of days of my life being hungover? Is it fun dealing with the ailments that drinking was giving me? Is it fun getting home in the early hours of the morning after spending the evening talking nonsense with people I don't even really know, spending money on damaging my own body? Something to look forward to? What, wasting money and time that could be better spent? Better social life? What, not remembering it? I like the taste. Drink the 0% options that are now available everywhere. I like how it makes me feel? Do I really? Or do I like the fact it tricks you into thinking your problems are removed, but actually it's compressing them and multiplying them?

I realised I had been trapped in a twenty-year cycle and, as the years have gone on, the alcohol consumption was less about fun and more about need. The stints of sobriety were giving me a taste of what life was like without it. I looked ahead with a different mindset. The man who stopped me outside the bar told me that I would have a successful life if I gave up my bad habits, I was thirty-seven years old, so I had potentially got fifty to sixty years left on this earth. If I gave up drinking, I would have all that time ahead to spend with my family, embracing every single day, feeling 100% all the time, setting a good example for my children to follow, being the beacon of change for any friends and family that may follow me.

On April 21st 2020, I woke up and decided that 'today is the day it stops'. I was going to enjoy all of those benefits of sobriety that I had written down every single day. No more self-sabotage, no more wasting time, energy and money. No more drinking through the stresses of life. I was going to start a new life and become the best version of myself, and the only thing that would prevent me from doing that was alcohol, so I was giving it up. I felt so excited, like the start of a new adventure and I was so excited to tell everyone the news. I knew it wasn't going to be easy, but with all the groundwork I had put in, I had given myself the best chance possible to succeed.

ALCOHOL – BETTER YOU

Now listen, this is the most difficult part of the journey, but the biggest changes make the biggest difference and if you are serious about becoming a better you then this one is critical. I'm yet to meet anyone who regrets giving up drinking and I don't think I ever will, but it's a difficult thing to do; no matter how much you drink, it's a big change to make. But my God it's worth it. If the thought of going sober forever is a bit daunting, why not try a twenty-eight-day challenge[1] or even three months. That way you can feel the benefits for yourself and then make bigger commitments further down the line. You don't have to give up drinking forever, giving yourself a decent period of time off will show you all you need to see and have you feeling incredible in a very short space of time.

---

1   Note – if you have history of heavy alcohol use, I advise contacting your GP before completely cutting out alcohol as you could be at risk of AWD (Alcohol Withdrawal Delirium).

Here are some of the top hints and tips that have helped me along the way with my sobriety.

How long do you want to give up for? It may seem strange to say, but in my experience the longer the time, the easier it is, as you can just get it out of the way and move on with life rather than looking forward to next week or the end of the month when you can have that drink. That said, you need to make sure that the timescale is achievable for yourself, but also long enough to really get the alcohol well out of your system and enjoy the benefits that brings.

Set yourself up a tracking system so you can count the days/ weeks that you are sober. This is such a great way to keep yourself motivated. It's really important to take it day by day in the early stages, so having the daily tally really helps to see the progression. I used the app "I am sober", which I would recommend. You could also use your journal to record how you are feeling each day.

Observe your danger zone. This means the time of day when you crave a drink the most, or maybe the time of day that you usually have a drink. Is it the weekend? After work? Whenever it is, it's important to recognise it and take precaution around that time. I call it the danger zone for a reason, you can be absolutely fine all day and then it can suddenly hit you out of nowhere and, if you aren't prepared, it's easy to slip up. Cover the danger zones with alcohol-free alternatives, or plan something into your schedule. My danger zone was after work and before dinner. I would have a diet cola when I got in from work, then eat my dinner earlier so that I minimised the time spent in the danger zone. Once I had eaten, I would plan something to do in the evening to make the most of the time, watching Netflix, going for a walk, writing this book or family video calls all worked for me.

Alcohol-free options are better than they have ever been, and they are FANTASTIC! Let's face it, most of the time it's the thought of having a drink that's often better than the actual process. So why not continue to drink alcohol-free alternatives and go through the same motions? You can really go to town and use a wine glass for AF wine, or a frozen pint glass for an AF beer. You can even get AF spirits now, which you can throw in a big goblet with loads of ice and a slice. You will be surprised how good they are and how much easier they make the transition.

Find a hobby, do something new, join a gym or just start going to the gym you joined ages ago and never go to! Drinking takes up so much time, you will find yourself with longer days and bags of free time. If you don't fill it proactively, you risk becoming bored and, if you get bored, you're more likely to drink. Not only that but how exciting to be given back so much time! What have you always wanted to do? Learn a language? Play the guitar? Get a qualification? Do it! Not only are you improving yourself, but you are also eliminating the risk of drinking.

Review who you are following on your social media; remember, we already discussed the importance of this earlier on. Think about adding some new people to follow that promote sobriety, or people that review alcohol-free drinks, or even more people that support your newfound hobby of the guitar or speaking Spanish. Whatever you do, just avoid the people who are always out drinking and partying; that will not be good for your willpower tank and it will subconsciously work against what you are trying to achieve.

Once you take a break from drinking, you are going to be feeling pretty amazing, very quickly. Make sure you enjoy that feeling! You are going to sleep much better than before; you are going to have more time and energy. You are going to be looking bright eyed and full of enthusiasm every morning. Smile, enjoy the feeling and embrace the new lifestyle. Don't ever look back and regret not doing it sooner, just be proud of yourself for doing it now. Watch your life progress at a speed you won't believe. Enjoy that feeling, you deserve it.

Hold yourself accountable for your sobriety, whether it's a week or a year, own this decision, tell the world, tell your friends and family that you are doing it and ask for their support. By telling your closest friends and family you are much more likely to achieve your target. if you can find someone who will do it with you then that's even better as you can support each other as well as hold each other accountable.

Do something new with your new self. Have you ever thought about going to visit that one place for the weekend? Or going to a detox retreat? Or going on that hike? Now is the time to do it, book it in and go. Going away for the weekend, the week or just the afternoon and exploring new places is just amazing. There is so much of the world to see and now you have the time, you wake up fresh and full of energy, there has never been a better time to go and explore. Take the kids to the woods, take your parents on a walk, take your dog on an adventure. Whatever you do, do something, you won't regret it.

Use this time of sobriety to spend quality time with the people who mean the most in your life. Being sober gives you more time to spend with loved ones, but it also gives you much more focus and clarity of thought, therefore your conversations become much more sincere and meaningful. You become a better listener and feel much more engaged than ever before. Reach out to your loved ones, go and visit them and spend some quality time nurturing those special relationships.

If you hang around with five smokers, you'll be the sixth, if you hang around with five runners, you'll be the sixth and if you hang around with five drinkers, you'll be the sixth. This is true in all walks of life, especially drinking. If you review your circle, you are likely to find it full of people who drink. By going sober you think it will be a problem, but this isn't necessarily the case. If the people in your circle are true friends, they will back you and support your decision. Regardless of the effect it has on them. Of course, you will have some friends that may take the piss and may not want to hang around with you anymore; they are clearly not someone you should be friends with anyway. But always be kind, as these are often the people who have a problem.

Go easy on yourself and take one day at a time. If you fall off, just jump straight back on again. It took me a number of attempts before I could even do two weeks off, but there is learning with every failure and it's all part of the journey.

When you take a break from alcohol or give up entirely, you will find yourself in an incredible position to take your life to a new level. Progression is infinite as you don't have that boozy night or weekend halting your progress, you just keep on moving forward all the time. Make sure you are always keeping that vision in your head crystal clear of the person you want to become. Only look forward, as that's the direction you are heading in.

ACTION

- Set yourself a clear goal for how long you are going to give up for.
- Track your progress by using an app or a calendar.
- Identify the danger zone and close it.
- Use alcohol-free alternatives.
- Start a new hobby to occupy your mind.
- Review who you are following on social media, try following some sober accounts.
- Enjoy the feeling of freshness every day.
- Give yourself enough time to sleep, your body will thank you for it.
- Do something spontaneous, you will have much more time and energy.
- Invest in yourself, you will be saving a lot of money, so reinvest it into you.
- Take one day at a time and go easy on yourself.

NUTRITION – BETTER ME

Growing up, my understanding of nutrition was pretty much non-existent. Fruit and vegetables were good, salt and sugar were bad, green salads were good, burgers and fries were bad, you get the picture. Not only was my nutritional knowledge poor, but I simply didn't care too much about it or have much understanding of how my diet had such a big impact on my energy levels, performance and mood. I just thought that food was food, it's there for enjoyment and fuel and nothing else. I never thought of exploring different food groups or experimenting with nutrition. My appetite was always big, and my preferences vast. I literally ate anything and everything.

But arriving in my thirties, I started to take more notice with my food choices. This was purely for vanity reasons as I didn't want to gain weight, but the more I educated myself and took notice of what I was eating, the more I started to really notice how different I felt after eating certain foods. Meat made me tired and lethargic every time I ate it, particularly red meat, whilst potatoes, pasta and rice would make me feel heavy and bloated. I never really thought about changing my diet, after all it's what I'd grown up with, but it was an awareness that I hadn't had before.

When Rocco died, drinking became my priority over my eating. When I did eat, I would make something that was quick and easy or order a takeaway of some sort. At the worst time in my life, I was eating the worst kind of food I'd ever eaten, I was drinking the most alcohol I had ever drunk and, as a result, it was affecting my mood, my weight and I was not sleeping at all. The cycle continued for months, the weight was creeping up and it was driving me into a spiral that was becoming out of control.

When I started to take strategic breaks from alcohol, my diet would automatically improve. I had eaten and drunk so much shit for such a long time that I started to crave nutritious food and looked forward to drinking lots of water. The more I was eating nutritious food, the better I was feeling and, for the first time in my life, I started to feel the benefit of what I was eating in my energy levels, digestion and clarity of thought. Alongside the not drinking, it made for a perfect storm, and I started to get some good quality sleep for the first time in months.

I got excited and started to grow in confidence. I wanted to have more variety in my diet. For my whole life I had pretty much eaten the same food, ordered the same takeaway and felt the same physically and mentally from doing so. But the more I started experimenting with different vegetables, beans, legumes and fruits, the better I started to feel. I started to cut down on my meat consumption and felt much better for doing so. It was at a time where there was a trend that had started called meat-free Mondays, a commitment that you eat no meat at all in any of your meals on that day of the week. This seemed a fairly simple concept but considering I ate meat in pretty much all of my meals it was going to take some getting used to.

Mondays are generally long and boring, so I wanted to make something interesting and new to eat for dinner to incorporate some variety. Meat-free Monday was great fun, interesting and really educational for me. I learned so much about the way in which meat can be replicated with vegetables and it made me feel better in myself, gave me much more energy and I felt as though I was doing the right thing for the planet, which was aligning me more and more with my new self. Meat-free Mondays spread into meat-free Tuesdays and a few months later I made the decision to live meat free every day. It was a no brainer for me. I felt better, it was helping my energy levels, I felt leaner and I was enjoying the food, so I found it all very easy.

When I started to merge my non-drinking spells with my new meat-free life, the weight started to shift, which was an even bigger incentive to carry on with both changes. I felt like I was a saint, looking down at anyone eating fast food or cake, whilst I was counting the calories on the bottom of my quinoa. But when I was drinking, it was a very different story. I wouldn't give a shit about calorie counting and I wouldn't think twice about eating some greasy food on the way home from the pub either. Living life in such extreme contrasts made me realise how much better I was feeling on the healthy side of life, which helped me decide I was going to go sober. That was when my nutrition really stepped up a level. It wasn't just the empty calories from the alcohol that I was saving, but the stodgy food on the way home stopped, the greasy breakfasts the morning after stopped and everything got better. I had real momentum and even if I had a bit of an indulgence over the weekend I would still go into Monday with amazing energy and motivation to be healthy for the week ahead.

Where I had been tracking calories and watching what I eat on non-drinking days beforehand, I started tracking them every day. I set myself a goal of losing two stone, which was something I never thought was possible before because I knew that my drinking would always stunt any real progression I was making from a weight perspective. But now it felt achievable; in fact, it almost felt easy because I had released that ball and chain from around my ankle and I was on the move fast.

I realised how much I had been abusing my body by feeding it so much crap over such a long time, sometimes out of laziness or 'hungover'-ness, but sometimes just out of a lack of awareness. I felt an amazing sense of gratification to my body, I couldn't believe it had adapted to putting up with so much abuse and still had the decency to work! I went on a mission to give myself what I need every single day and give my body what it deserved. I tracked everything I ate and drank to see my calorie intake, how much protein, fat and carbs I was consuming (Macros or macronutrients) and even how my micronutrients were stacking up.

This was kind of fun as I learnt so much over such a short period of time. If my iron was deficient for a day, I would google "what meat-free food is high in iron?" I would then buy that food, eat it and then punch it in the app to see how much the bar filled up. There was something seriously satisfying about getting it nailed at the end of each day. I started to experiment with supplements, such as multivitamins. I would put these into the app and see all the macro bars jump up and I hadn't even eaten anything. As a non-meat-eater I was constantly short of B12 and iron, so they were what I would regularly supplement.

With alcohol out of the situation, my love of food grew stronger than ever, and I had a new appreciation for it. The process of eating became much more conscious, and I would savour every mouthful, try and ignite my senses and eat in a much more mindful manner. I suppose that everything just slowed down. I started to plan my food for the day in advance and ensure that I was balancing my macros throughout the day. By making my own food and taking it to work, I knew exactly what I was eating each day and I could track it all before I had even eaten it.

I started to experiment with fad weight loss diets in the hope of getting my weight down even faster. Each one added more education on what not to do rather than any of them actually providing a result. I think there is always value and learning in every diet I have ever tried, but what I realised over time is that the only diet that is going to work for me is one that is sustainable, enjoyable and flexible. I wanted to focus on building a nutritional plan that I could fit into my lifestyle, that made me feel great, that wasn't restrictive and gave me the flexibility to enjoy myself when I wanted to. So, I started to adopt a simple but effective method, putting myself in a calorie deficit.

For years I had been searching for that diet that was going to solve all of my problems and enable me to lose weight fast, but having allowed myself to do some research on weight loss, I realised that it really is as simple as just being in a calorie deficit. I had previously put myself on some crazy diets in the name of vanity, not helped by the latest celebrity celery diet or the juice detox method, or a new skinny tea being thrown in our faces online; it is so easy to get sucked into it. But in reality, the fundamental basics of weight management are centred around your individual calorie intake, making sure you have a balanced diet of carbohydrates, protein and fat, trying to take in as many micronutrients as possible throughout each day, staying hydrated and moving your body. It's really not that hard.

The reason I had been chasing different diets beforehand was because I was looking for a quick fix. This was also the reason why I drank or took drugs — it's a shortcut to the desired end result. I was always so impatient to get the results I wanted, and in today's swipe culture society there seems a need for speed in everything we do. But now I was more consciously aware of what was happening in my life, I had the ability to reflect on my own previous behaviour when it came to my nutrition. I would do one of these fad diets, I would lose 5lb over a week or so and feel like I had it all under control, then put it back on again over the next few weeks, then try another fast diet or heavily restricting my calorie intake over a short period of time to get it back under control again. It's the cycle of doom.

My mindset had changed, and I could think clearly. I could look at what I wanted my relationship to be like with food and drink, I could select what body I wanted to have rather than constantly fighting the flab. With a clear vision and a solid plan and, without the distraction of drinking, I got on with it. I've never been someone who wants to have huge muscles, I like to work out in general but my dream body is lean, toned and fit rather than big, pumped and strong, and with my desire of building everything in my life with sustainability in mind, my body goal required a balanced diet, with no need to eat an excessive amount of protein for muscle growth and no need to avoid our beloved carbs as I will be exercising regularly.

To do something sustainably it's really important I enjoy it and it's not too restrictive. Having been someone who was eating such a limited variety of food throughout my life, I really wanted to maintain that diverse approach in my nutritional plan. I am also a huge fan of treating myself at the weekend, so now that I had given up drinking, I wanted to make sure that I wasn't being too restrictive and able to have a bit of a blow out without totally pressing the fuck it button and ruining any progress.

My plan was simple, it was the good old 80/20 rule, eat healthy for 80% of the time and allow 20% for a bit of a cheat day. The main thing was for it all to be enjoyable, eating healthy really doesn't have to be boring.

I now look forward to eating well more than I look forward to eating badly because I have educated myself on the effects eating processed, fatty, sugary food has on my body and I feel those effects physically and mentally when I indulge in a bit of a cheat meal. That said, I still love a cheat day for so many reasons. I feel much more sociable catching up with friends or family over a pizza rather than an apple and I think it's important for the kids to see both sides of the story, to feel okay about eating fatty sugary foods at times but focusing on eating whole, natural foods during the week.

NUTRITION – BETTER **YOU**

'm not writing this book to transform everyone that reads it into a sober plant eater, I am asking you to take an interest in what you are putting into your body. You wouldn't intentionally put the wrong fuel in your car, and I don't imagine that you would smash the window or kick a dent in it either, so why do we do it to ourselves? Because you can't see the damage, that's probably why.

Your body is amazing, a complete fucking miracle. Think about it... How amazing are we as humans? We have been so blessed to get a shot at this game called life and we have been provided with one hell of a vehicle to use and yet everyone at some point in their lives takes their body for granted. If I gave you a doughnut or a can of pop, most people would thank me and see that as a treat or a reward, but in fact it's not good for us, it has a negative effect on your sustained energy and mood, it will raise your blood sugar levels, it's bad for your teeth, etc. So why do we eat it and why do we see that as a treat? Give your body the respect it deserves and feed it as much natural whole foods as possible.

I read about eating whole food years ago and it's stuck with me ever since. It makes so much sense to make as much of your diet whole foods as possible. Whole foods are literally what they say on the tin, foods that are whole, i.e. not tampered with or processed, such as fruit, vegetables, meat, fish, nuts and seeds. The benefits are that they are packed with nutrients, naturally high in vitamins, minerals and fibre.

The more whole foods you can incorporate into your diet, the better your body will function and if you are aiming to be a better you then this is a really important step, as it will not only help you to look and feel better but you will be able to function at a higher level over a sustained period of time. I aim to hit the 80/20 rule daily, eating whole foods 80% of the time but allowing 20% for anything else. But the more I eat whole foods the better I feel, so it's not uncommon for me to go days just eating whole food.

Drink more water. The world is seriously dehydrated and it's another common own goal that you must take seriously. Your body is mostly water, so the importance of keeping yourself hydrated is obvious when you think of it like that. You are supposed to drink six to eight glasses of water per day, which is so easy in principle but so difficult in reality. As if that wasn't hard enough, we are consuming more alcohol and coffee than ever before, which actually dehydrates you, meaning that six to eight glasses still aren't enough. If you exercise you lose fluids, so you need to drink even more. Even flying can cause dehydration due to the dry air that you inhale, so hydration whilst flying is also key. If you are dehydrated you will experience effects on your body such as headaches, feeling tired and lethargic, constipation, with low mood and lack of clarity, plus your pee will stink and nobody will like you. Kidding, but seriously, stay hydrated – it's important.

Are you one of those people who are always trying out the latest diet? Are you one of those people who are constantly trying to eat well or "be good"? If that's not you then you will definitely be able to think of plenty of people close to you who are always on a diet. That was me too, until I realised that the people close to me who are always on a diet are the most overweight people I know, whereas the people closest to me who seemingly had few restrictions in their diet were never on a diet. Diets are for occasions, apart from that, they are never going to solve your weight problems. If you need to lose 8lb to look good at your sister's wedding or even your own, then you crack on with the diet. If you have booked a holiday with four weeks' notice and you think 'oh shit, I need to lose weight fast', then a hard and fast way to do it is through a low-calorie diet.

What if you could live a life whereby you enjoy ALL the food you eat EVERY DAY and you NEVER have to go on a diet again, how incredible would that be? Well, that is exactly what you can do with a bit of patience and discipline. Calorie control is my go-to when it comes to weight management. If you consume more than you burn, you put on weight and if you consume less than you burn then you lose weight. It really can be that simple, but it takes a bit of experimenting to get the best results and you need to know what your calorie intake should be to ensure that you increase, decrease or maintain your weight, depending on your nutritional goal.

There are two useful bits of information you can go and find out at the touch of a button, assuming you know your most recent height and weight – if you don't then you can get a set of good digital scales online super cheap these days. They are your BMR and your TDEE. Don't worry, they sound much more complicated than they are, and I'll explain them to the best of my ability.

Basal Metabolic Rate calculator or BMR. This is the number of calories your body burns while at rest. This number will help you determine your caloric needs. It gives you an exact number based on numerous factors such as your age, height, weight and activity level. In other words, it's the minimum number of calories your body needs to function. For me, it's 1800, which seems a lot if I think of myself as doing nothing all day, but you forget the amount of energy internally that is required to keep your blood pumping and heart beating.

Then you have Total Daily Energy Expenditure (TDEE), which is basically your BMR plus your estimated energy expenditure on everything you do on a daily basis such as walking the dog, taking a shower or doing the dishes; it also accounts for your activity level. Again, this is just an online calculator. This gives you more of a target number of calories to consume per day and the simple science behind that number means that technically if you exceed the daily number then you will put on weight and if you consume less than that number then you lose weight.

Now, like anything in life, that is very subjective and how accurate that calculation is will be dependent on what it is that you are eating, whether you are moving your body as much as you said you were in the calculation, whether you are resting well, whether you are hydrated, etc., but it's a great place to start and I like to keep things simple. If nothing else, it gives you an awareness of your daily intake needs and that is something that most people are unaware of.

My advice is purely based on my own experience and that is not to restrict your diet so much that you feel like you need a cheat day. Consciously choosing to eat unhealthy meals is very different to needing to pig out because you haven't been eating a healthy balanced diet. There is absolutely nothing wrong with enjoying a pizza and some ice cream on a Saturday night; as long as you stay disciplined for 80% of your week, you can go and enjoy that dirty meal or two. I certainly do.

ACTION

- Identify your BMR and TDEE to understand what your daily calorie intake should be.
- Now hit that target by eating as much whole food as you can.
- No food is out of the question, but just keep to the 80/20 rule.
- Use supplements to bridge the gap to any nutrients you may be lacking.
- Try not to eliminate any of your macros, instead opt for a balance across all three (carbohydrates, protein and fat).
- Enjoy everything that you eat.
- By eating well, you will transform your mind and be able to think clearer and concentrate longer, giving you improved results personally and professionally.

EXERCISE – BETTER ME

I was fortunate enough not to have to consciously do any exercise until my twenties because I was so obsessed with playing football at every possible opportunity, which was a continuous source of movement. However, once the football days finished, I got into that classic dad bod mentality of thinking I was still fit, but physically the beers and burgers had started to take their toll. Once exercise was something I knew I HAD to do rather than something I did because I enjoyed it, I started to resent it and looked at it as an effort rather than looking at the benefits it gave me.

I first joined a gym at the age of eighteen. It was one of those posh ones with a swimming pool and a restaurant, both of which I used a lot more than the gym itself, but I felt a sense of superiority just by having the membership card in my wallet. My theory was that if I join a gym that looks good and feels inspiring it will motivate me to go more often. It didn't. I would follow the oh so familiar pattern of going almost every day for the first month, then a couple of times a week for the second month, then barely going at all for month three, then forgetting about it.

These gyms or 'health clubs' are also fucking expensive, which worked against me as I felt a sense of pressure to go because I wanted my money's worth. But that pressure just resulted in me not wanting to go and the cycle of absence continued. I then went through the next decade joining different gyms, thinking that the location must be the issue rather than the ever-increasing alcohol consumption and the poor diet that was suffocating me slowly both physically and mentally.

The less I exercised, the less I wanted to exercise. My ever-expanding waistline and my additional chin count were having the opposite effect on my motivation to move my body and I started to get into the 'fuck it I'm overweight and that's what happens at my age' mindset, which is a path well-trodden but not one I ever thought I would walk. The fact is my priorities started to change. I was a husband and a father, and I was doing what most men do at that stage of their life, working hard and providing for the family, and if you get any spare time, you spend it drinking beer as quickly as possible. Exercise had dropped down the pecking order and continued to do so up until after Rocco died.

I didn't do any exercise for a year or so after losing Rocco, but as I started to come out of the haze that I was stuck in during that first year, I felt a strong, almost aggressive urge to want to do something charitable in his name, something that would provide me with a sense of purpose and something I could really focus on. I signed up to the London Marathon in 2015 with a charity called the Lullaby Trust who raise awareness of sudden infant death syndrome, which is what Rocco died from. I was overweight, unfit and completely fed up with feeling so bad all the time and I knew the best thing I could do was exercise. With an event like the London Marathon to inspire me, it was the perfect way to get me going.

Running a marathon had always been on my bucket list, but it had never got very far from leaving that list. Now was the perfect time to do it. I had been a lifelong viewer of the London Marathon, from a boy watching it on the TV with my parents to a man going to watch it every year in the flesh, it's an event like no other. Every year the crowd and the atmosphere are electric but it's the emotion that makes the day so special. Everyone is running it for a reason, most of which are tragic, which just makes it feel as though it's one big family and the level of support for one and other is something very special. Even watching from the sidelines pulls you into the emotion of the occasion, but running it myself was going to be a different level.

Throughout my adult life, whilst on any kind of health kick or diet, my go-to form of exercise was always running. Whether it was on a treadmill or outdoors, it was the one thing I knew I could do and, despite my increasingly heavier frame and my slower timings, I quite liked it. The mental benefits were just as good as the physical ones, and I knew that it was just what I needed, so I was excited to get stuck into my marathon training programme.

The first few runs were a real eye opener for me, a real marker of how much I had neglected my health, body and fitness in general. But despite this harrowing self-realisation, the progression was surprisingly fast, and I knew that the only way was up. I signed up for lots of smaller running events for the weeks and months that followed, which were great for my motivation and broke down the rather intimidating sixteen-week programme into achievable bite-sized chunks.

Running also gave me something to think about even when I wasn't doing it: What route will I take next time? How long will it take me? How far can I push myself? Who will I run with? All these thoughts were giving me a focus that was most definitely needed. I became obsessed with my training plan, and I stuck to it religiously. Going from not running at all to running a marathon within six months is a really big ask and one that requires a lot of planning and discipline, both of which were exactly what I needed in my life.

Motivating myself to get out and run was one thing, but there were some times when I started and just couldn't comprehend the distance ahead of me. Some days were easy, and I would barely even have to think about it, but other days were tough, and I had to break through my self-limitations, one step at a time, mile after mile. I knew I had no excuse to stop, but I was also in unknown territory. Every Sunday my long run would finish, and I would be feeling really proud of myself and my efforts. Every week I hit a new landmark as the runs became longer and longer. The scale of the challenge really built up as the training progressed, but I was so determined to get through it I managed to get each run in the bag and built up to the big day.

The day of the marathon came around fast. I'd love to tell you that it was amazing, and I enjoyed every minute of it, but in truth I was a complete mess. Not because of lack of training but because I was just so desperately emotional. Six months of dedication and focus all building up to this day, running it in memory of my son with all of my family watching who were as emotional as I was, it was all too much. But through grit and determination I managed to finish it, thanks mainly to the amazing support all around the city, particularly from my family who were scattered at various cheering points along the route. My cousin Kelly came over from America to run it with me and without her I'm not sure I would have finished it. All of my training seemed to go out of the window as I almost broke down with emotion crossing the finishing line.

Following the marathon, I decided to give myself a break from any kind of exercise. My days, evenings and weekends had been entirely consumed with marathon training and I wanted to have some time out before putting the running shoes back on. That was a big mistake as I didn't put them back on for three years. During those three years, my grief took over and I lost myself to the pull of alcohol, which further demotivated me from doing any exercise. Where I had previously used running as an output for my emotion, I now used alcohol and life went from bad to worse as I struggled to deal with my grief. It wasn't until I got divorced, left my family home and met my now wife that life began to recover and, in the process, so did my exercise routine.

As my recovery journey gathered pace, I started to realise how much I had abused my body and how unfit I had become. I felt terrible and I looked even worse, so I decided that I wanted to join a gym (again). I wanted to do something that would spark my love for exercise back into life, but it wasn't going to be running as I was still scared from the emotional twenty-six miles I had done a few years before. I decided to do some spin classes, spending time in an air-conditioned studio with loud music and really nice people, whilst burning calories, what a great combination.

I started to realise that my best results were when I bolted exercise onto my breaks from alcohol, as this then made me more aware of my nutrition, which also improved. As a result of all three improvements, I was sleeping better than ever. When I exercised, focused on my nutrition, drank no alcohol and slept well I felt incredible, but this wasn't very often, as all it took was a boozy event at work or someone's birthday drinks and I was right back in a rut. But once I had a glimpse of what life could be like at my optimum self, I wanted more of it.

I started using my newfound love of reading and learning to increase my knowledge of why we should exercise, the benefits to our body and also the different types of exercise. I found out about something called NEAT exercise, which I found fascinating. NEAT exercise stands for Non-Exercise Activity Thermogenesis, and in simple terms this means calories you burn from movement such as hoovering, shopping, walking up the stairs or washing the dishes, basically anything outside of traditional structured exercise. I had no idea how many calories I could burn during the basic activities of life.

This encouraged me to take the stairs rather than the lift, to walk rather than take the Tube and to make sure I was getting my 10,000 steps in per day. I was trying to fit NEAT exercise in at every opportunity alongside the structured exercise I had started to enjoy at the gym. It was all going really well for a few weeks and the year of 2020 was looking really positive. Although I was still drinking and having the odd blow out at the weekend, I had become more aware than ever before about the benefits of exercise, as well as the damage that alcohol and a bad diet was having. I realised that if I wanted to really optimise my life, I needed to have consistency and progression, both of which were a problem because of alcohol. The decision was an obvious one and, once I gave up drinking, my relationship with exercise changed dramatically.

I instantly slept better, which meant I woke up fresh and motivated every single day. My nutrition improved consistently, which meant I had more energy when exercising. When I exercised I was burning more calories, which meant my weight started dropping. When my weight dropped, my performance improved, and when my performance improved it gave me more confidence, and when I felt more confident I was more motivated to keep going, as the results in all areas of my physical well-being were significantly improving. Now I was exercising because I wanted to, not because I had to.

I started to run again and I loved it. I set myself challenges to run faster or longer. One month I ran 100km, the next month stepped it up to 100 miles within the month (160km) and I achieved that with relative ease. With my newfound progression, I was taking chunks off of my PBs over all distances. I was running better and faster than ever in my life at the age of thirty-seven, but more importantly I was enjoying every minute of it.

The kids all picked up on my energy and enthusiasm for running and they all became interested in taking part. This was another benefit that I hadn't considered. I had really thought about the fact I wanted my boys to grow up with their dad not drinking so they would hopefully avoid doing so when they grew up, but I hadn't thought of how much they would follow in my footsteps so quickly when it came to running and exercise. They say that kids will seldom do as you say, but they will always do what you do.

I was adamant I would incorporate exercise into my schedule and make it happen regardless of what would get in the way. As I mentioned in my habit stacking section, I built a framework that incorporated everything I needed to perform at my optimum level, and running was built in on Tuesdays, Thursdays and Saturdays. This was really achievable and spread out nicely throughout the week. Monday was an early start for me in London and Friday was Friday, so I was happy I could sustain this pattern, and I did. Tuesday and Thursday were either a thirty-minute home workout in front of the TV or a 5km run. Saturday was a 10km route, the same route every week. I had found that 10km was a good distance for me, not too short but long enough to push myself. It also gave me some time alone to enjoy being outside whilst educating myself with an eBook or a podcast.

Exercising before work was something that I had never done before, at least not for any consistent length of time. I had been missing out big time. I couldn't believe how putting thirty minutes aside at the start of the day completely changed my mindset for the day ahead. Where I thought it would make me tired, it actually gave me much more energy throughout the whole day. As a result, everything else for the day followed suit; my food choices were much more considered, my concentration level improved and I had a real spring in my step.

My performance at work improved significantly. I was arriving earlier than ever before glowing with energy and with complete clarity on what needed to be achieved. My focus and concentration had been something I had always struggled with for any prolonged time but adding exercise into my routine gave me the clarity I had longed for.

Now with my exercise routine well absorbed into my schedule, alongside my other areas of personal improvement – sleep, alcohol-free and nutrition – as well as the incorporation of NEAT exercise and walking 10,000 steps a day, for the first time in my life I can say that I am fit, healthy and more importantly HAPPY.

EXERCISE – BETTER YOU

D o you think we evolved this far to sit at a desk in a nine-to-five job every day, not giving ourselves time to move our body? Instead, we go home tired and lethargic because we haven't moved enough, and guess what we want to do? Relax and sit down some more. And how does that make us feel? Tired and lethargic! And what happens when we go to work the next day? You guessed it, we feel tired and lethargic, so we stimulate ourselves with caffeine and drag ourselves through the day using mealtimes as milestones until we can go home and repeat.

I have some good news, you already do exercise, but you just don't count it. Do you walk to your car? Brush your teeth? Go to the bathroom? Well, these are all a form of NEAT exercise, and you can use these examples to help kickstart your new life to include exercise. Think about taking your phone calls whilst on the move, you can plan in a call with your friends or family at the weekend and talk while you walk. Chances are you won't even notice you are exercising whilst engrossed in your call. Any level of exercise is good for you.

Think how lucky you are to be able to do any form of exercise at all. Exercise is a privilege and something we should be grateful to be able to do. Whether it's walking to the shop or running a marathon, it's all exercise and it's all working towards optimising every part of your life. Exercise is as important to the mind as it is to the body.

There are a variety of different types of exercise that you could consider doing. Endurance training, such as walking, cycling or running are seen by many as your traditional forms of exercise. Strength training can be anything from lifting weights to using resistance exercises to increase strength, muscle mass and bone density, amongst other things. Balance exercise is predominantly to build strength and increase stability. Flexibility exercises can be something as simple as stretching, but more commonly yoga or tai chi. You just need to try them and see what feels most natural to you.

Do what you enjoy doing, not what you think you have to do or what you think will bring you the best results. I've covered the different types of exercise, but as you are also aware, there are plenty of ways to exercise. What do you enjoy doing? Maybe you like spending time with people socially so you could join a club of some description, such as running or cycling? Maybe dig out your boots and join a local sports team? Maybe you like being alone, so you could start running or cycling? Have a look a bit further outside the conventional forms of exercise. Boxing is a great sport to get into as it teaches discipline and mental strength as much as it is amazing for your physical health, and it doesn't even need to include getting punched in the face if you don't want it to.

You could take up dancing with a partner. There is a rise in popularity for more adventurous forms of exercise like pole dancing, hiking and rock climbing. I could go on and on but you get the point. There are so many ways to do some kind of workout from home, especially with the accessibility of YouTube. There you will find any form of exercise you can possibly need from boxercise to HIIT workouts, most of which require no equipment, so there is another excuse you can let go of.

Signing up for an event of some description is a great way of motivating yourself to get on with it. So many events are free to do, and they are a great way to get out and meet people as well as benefitting you physically and mentally. Take a look online at different events that are taking place near you in six months' time and give yourself plenty of notice. Maybe get a friend to join you and you can train for it together.

Signing up for something will give you the excitement that will help you get started. It will also give you an immense feeling of satisfaction once you have done it and a strange feeling of wanting to sign up for more in the future. Doing something for charity is also a great motivator and another way to give yourself the feel-good factor.

Personally, I can't recommend running highly enough. It's free to do and you don't need any equipment except some running shoes. If you are feeling bad mentally, it will make you feel better, if you feel good mentally, it will make you feel better. If you feel stressed, go for a run, if you have a craving, go for a run. You can go as far or as short as you want to, and you can run in pretty much all weather, so there really is no excuse. There are tons of events you can do yourself, such as Couch to 5km, where it gives you a training plan that instructs you on how to get from being a couch potato to running 5km over a set period of time. That then opens the door to starting parkrun, for example, which is a fantastic event held all around the world for free. You might then get a taste for it and want to sign up for a 10km event, then another one to try and improve your time, then maybe a half marathon or even a full marathon.

We have all been there, New Year's day, signing up for a gym membership that will end up costing you a fortune as you will keep it running in the false promise to yourself that you will go; next week turns into next month and before you know it you are admitting defeat and cancelling the thing, making all the excuses in the world for why that wasn't a good gym, or why the class timetable doesn't work with your availability, whereas in reality we have had our priorities in other parts of our lives that don't particularly sit well alongside the gym life.

Don't fall into the trap of aimlessly joining a gym without having a goal in mind first. There is nothing worse than seeing that money come out of your account and feeling like you HAVE to go. This will only deter you from exercising and adopt a negative perception of the gym. Change your mindset and see it as a privileged position to be in. Visits to the gym can be very sociable and a great way of meeting like-minded people, but they can also be great for people who need the discipline of visiting a venue where they are there to do one thing and one thing only.

Whatever exercise you decide to do, make sure you are tracking your progress. Whether it's via an app like Strava or the Nike running app or by investing in a smart watch, which gives you another level of information on your workouts. Chances are your phone is recording your step count and you don't even look at it. You will be amazed at the motivation you get from looking back at what you have achieved, as well as using it to work on improving your distance or performance.

ACTION

- Exercise to feel good, not because you think you have to.
- Choose a form of exercise that you enjoy, not one that other people enjoy.
- Be consistent, make sure you build the time into your schedule.
- Start small and work your way up.
- Incorporate as much NEAT exercise into your day as possible.
- Try to hit 10,000 steps every day.
- Exercise with friends or family to help with the motivation.
- Try and get your exercise done in the morning where possible as that's when you will get the best quality of workout, plus you are less likely to cancel your exercise plans in the morning.
- Join a club like a running club, cycling club or dancing club. That way you get the social benefits and build friendships along the way.
- Sign up for an event in the future to give yourself something to work towards.
- Only join a gym if you really enjoy the atmosphere and will feel motivated and inspired to visit.
- Track your progress by using a smart watch or an app.

SLEEP – BETTER ME

'You can sleep when you're dead' used to be my favourite phrase when I was trying to persuade the last remaining people in the pub to stay with me. As much as I loved sleeping when I was younger and knew that I functioned better when I had it in good measure, my relationship with sleep started to change as my drinking increased. Drinking used to knock me flat out, but I would always then wake up in the early hours of the morning needing the bathroom. After that I knew I was in trouble. All my thoughts would hit me like a train, I'd have a dull headache as the hangover started to creep in and I would be gasping for a drink.

The more I drank the more often this happened and the more it happened the more I started to associate sleeping as a painful experience rather than an important necessity.

When I was in a particularly bad place mentally, I used to dread the thought of going to bed, as I knew that was the time when I was cornered with nowhere to go, so I would make sure that I carried on drinking until I was at the stage of passing out just to get off to sleep. But if the drinking didn't knock me out, I could lay there for hours with my thoughts racing around my head. The more it would stress me out, the more I would struggle to sleep. With every glance at the clock, it was another hour into the night and another hour closer to me having to get up, get sorted and get on the train to work.

I spent so many nights just lying there thinking 'fuck it, I'm just going to get up. I might as well, as I can't sleep'. Most mornings I would wake up at about 3am and face the decision of whether to make a cup of coffee or a vodka and coke. Some nights I would take sleeping pills to knock me out so that I could just function the following day, but even they didn't work after a while.

When I started my recovery and took a break from drinking, I slept like a baby. The better sleep I was having, the better I became as a person, the more I was feeling better as a person, the more I was investing my time in personal development, and this is where my view of sleeping started to change. Anyone I was inspired by in the personal development space would always talk about sleep as being one of the most important skills to master when becoming the best version of ourselves. Podcasts, books, websites, they would all say the same thing, sleep is one of the highest priorities in their lifestyle. But often the one that gets ignored.

I had a burning desire to improve my life, and I knew how good I felt when I hadn't had a drink and had a good night's sleep, so I knew that they were right. But it was only when I took a break from alcohol for a few weeks that I started to see the real benefit to it. Waking up feeling fresh and rested every day felt amazing and my performance in all areas of my life flourished. Especially because I had become so accustomed to waking up feeling like a complete sack of shit most mornings.

I read a book called *Sleep* by Nick Littlehales, who had been previously recruited as a sleep coach by Sir Alex Ferguson when he was managing Manchester United in a time when they were dominating the world soccer scene. He then went on to help a variety of elite sports teams across the world in order to help them to be the best and stay the best. I couldn't believe that was a thing. There I was, telling myself that I wanted to be something in life, whilst scoring a huge own goal.

Once I gave up drinking completely, my relationship with sleep transformed and I vowed never to neglect the importance of sleep again. Now I take pride in the fact that I go to bed early. If it gets past ten o'clock, I get a bit twitchy. By going to bed early and getting a full night's sleep, I can get up early and enjoy the best hours of the day as the sun rises.

SLEEP – BETTER YOU

We spend a third of our life asleep, so learning to pay it respect is going to benefit you throughout the other two thirds significantly.

If you want to be the best, then take a look at the best. Do you think that the top sports players in the world compromise on their sleep quantity and quality? It's one of their non-negotiables because sleeping has such a profound effect on our daily lives.

You are supposed to sleep for seven to nine hours per night depending on age, lifestyle, activity level, but the interesting thing about the duration of your sleep is that you are in a sleep cycle that lasts ninety minutes at a time, which consists of different stages. You go from being awake into light sleep, then deep sleep, then the final stage is something called the REM stage, which stands for Rapid Eye Movement because, fairly obviously, your eyes move rapidly.

It is in the REM stage of the cycle that a lot of the magic happens, such as memory consolidation and learning. Memory consolidation is so important as without it you are preventing your brain from being able to receive new information and make new memories. Think of it as your receptionist. Your REM sleep is where your brain gets to work and files all of your paperwork, leaving you a nice clear inbox in the morning. But if you don't get enough REM sleep then your inbox will already be full and the new information you try and put in there will just fall out.

The amount of REM sleep you have increases in every ninety-minute cycle; around 10% of your first cycle will be spent in the REM stage, whereas that percentage will get increasingly higher for each cycle you go through. Therefore, the more cycles you can get in, the more REM sleep you will have. The final cycle can give you around an hour of REM sleep, so the progression is vast.

Alcohol and sleeping may appear as though they go hand in hand but don't be fooled by the initial passing out stage. Research shows that if you consume alcohol, it reduces the amount of REM sleep you have. It also messes up your internal body clock, which means you are far more likely to wake up at irregular times during the night.

Aside from the significant medical reasons, lack of sleep will have serious knock-on effects to your nutrition, as you will crave sugar and carbohydrates and eat to excess as your ability to stop eating is compromised. Your mood will be affected, and your skin will age quicker.

In a nutshell, you need to make sleep a non-negotiable if you are serious about making big improvements in your life. To give yourself the best shot at a good night's sleep, you should avoid alcohol and caffeine, keep all of your personal devices out of the bedroom and stop using them for at least an hour before lights out. Create a routine for yourself to stick to every night. The better your routine, the better chance you have of getting a good night's sleep.

In my opinion, it is just as important to look at what you should do as well as what you should avoid in order to get a decent night's sleep. If you are getting up early and getting on with your day, doing some exercise and eating well, then you are going to significantly improve your sleeping ability for that night. If you then complement your healthy active day by avoiding everything listed above then you are onto a winner.

ACTION

- Learn to love your sleep. Sleeping is amazing and we often think of it as just something that needs to happen, rather than something we get to do.
- If you haven't fixed your mindset, nutrition and exercise routine and you are still drinking alcohol, you simply cannot get the quality of sleep needed to perform at your optimum level.
- Give sleep the respect it deserves.
- Make sure you get between seven and nine hours every night.
- Avoid caffeine after lunch.
- Limit the amount of screen time before you go to bed.
- Stick to a routine when going to bed and waking up.

SPIRITUALITY

"Spirituality does not come from religion. It comes from our soul."

Anthony Douglas Williams

The beautiful thing about spirituality is that there is no destination, it's an infinite journey of self-discovery and personal growth, which will also give you the ability to step outside of your mind and look at life through a much more peaceful lens. Spirituality beautifully wraps all of the content of this book together and enables you to reach new levels of happiness, peace and freedom. Who doesn't want that?

SPIRITUAL AWARENESS – BETTER ME

I f you had asked me what spirituality means a few years ago I would have said haunted houses, hippies and fortune tellers. I genuinely had no idea, and I don't think that many of my friends or family would have thought much different.

My mum used to visit a spiritualist from time to time and I just used to laugh and think it was a load of bullshit, but I always remember her being really moved by it every time she went. My sister then started to go with her as she got older, and she was equally impressed. They would come back and recite their reading to me, sometimes in tears of emotion and it would be pretty compelling to listen to what they had been told, but even then, I thought it was rubbish and that I knew better.

It was only when Rocco died that I thought 'fuck it, I'm going to give it a try'. I was at a complete loss and, having seen how much my mum and sister were getting from it previously, I went for it. I still didn't really associate myself as tapping into the spiritual world, as it was someone doing it for me. But, following that encounter, I had a different view entirely of the spiritual world and started to pay it much more respect.

The comfort I got from knowing that Rocco was okay and he was happy in the spiritual world was heart-warming. But I guess the real win from the experience was my awakening to the world of spirituality. The realisation that there are in fact people looking after me and you that we don't even know about. The other example I shared was years later at my rock bottom moment outside the pub, having been kicked out of my own house and unable to see what to do next. After receiving such clear instructions on what to do with my life, I started the process of rebuilding it. Without that experience on that day, I wouldn't like to think where I would be right now or if I would even be here at all.

They say when the heart breaks the heart opens, and on reflection that is exactly what happened to me. I didn't know it at the time, but this was the start of my spiritual awakening. I started to be much more open minded to spirituality as my journey of recovery started; I started to learn what spirituality means. What does it mean when you believe there is more to life than just our three-dimensional experience? This is when I learned that spirituality is about becoming aware of things outside of yourself, taking an interest in others and feeling fulfilled when doing so. It's about appreciating other people and what they bring into your life, it's becoming aware of nature and feeling a connection with it, it's about wanting to help other people and contribute towards the people and things that are right in the world. It's about helping us grow as a generation and leading our children and our children's children into a beautiful future.

I could track my spiritual journey right back to when Rocco died. After a year or so I had a really strong desire to raise money and help other people, which is when I signed up to run the London Marathon. Not long after that I took a keen interest in gardening and specifically plants, which was really fucking weird for someone who was also drinking heavily and sniffing cocaine. I started to enjoy going for walks and just being out amongst nature. This was something I had never enjoyed doing previously and would have never classed as being spiritual, but now I know it was exactly that, it made a lot of sense.

Another part of my spiritual journey was wanting to learn, which started by me taking an interest in nature documentaries and specifically how we as humans are killing our own planet and eating our own animals. For my entire life I had barely watched any documentaries and was a big meat eater, but I felt the need to educate myself and understand what I could do to help. I felt a connection to the earth and a connection to the animals, I was more aware of what I was doing and felt an instant need to change my behaviour. This all just came out of nowhere and, before I knew it, I was interested in finding out about the carbon footprint of the animal agriculture industry. That was what led me on my path of personal development, reading and learning.

The more spiritually connected I became, the more I appreciated everything I had in my life, in particular my health. My life had consisted of going to the gym and going on a diet to fight the flab, but never had I thought about doing it from an appreciation perspective or just to look after my body. I had battered it for years, treating it with barely any respect and having no gratitude for it still fully functioning despite everything I had thrown at it. But now it was different, now I was overwhelmingly grateful for every part of it, my organs for still working, my bones for being intact, my hair for still being there in abundance, my sight, hearing, teeth. You name it, I was grateful for it.

Spirituality made the decision to go sober so much easier. I was no longer as stressed out because I had learnt to be grateful. It also gave me this sense of happiness and peace that I had never experienced before, therefore I had less of a requirement to drink. I wanted to indulge in self-care and preservation, overcompensating for all the years of abuse that had taken place, so drinking alcohol was a pretty obvious place to start. Plus, I started to notice that I was much more spiritually aware and connected throughout my periods of sobriety than I was when I was drinking, which is just another benefit of knocking it on the head.

Once I went sober, my awareness started to expand rapidly, and I started to see everything from what felt like an elevated position. I could see the way we were destroying the planet, the way we were fighting with each other and the unnecessary chaos that was causing across the world, but I also had a sense of responsibility of how I had taken part in all of that and I had a real internal feeling of wanting to rectify my past behaviour and to help others to see the light. It was almost like spirituality gave me the ability to zoom out of the chaos of the world and view things with a much more centred perspective. I lost the ability to fight for what I thought was right, or stand my ground in confrontation, I just wanted to focus on what I can do to help everyone climb out of the chaos and into a world of connection and enlightenment.

Since going sober, my spiritual journey has gone from strength to strength. No more hungover meditations or going for a walk to get some fresh air, it's all about meditating because I love to do it and enjoy the process; going for walks on my own and being alone with nature is magical. I have completely changed the way I look at what's important in life. No longer is it the materialistic things that motivate me, now I am living authentically with an appreciation for what's important in life; health and family, nature and connection, wholeness and unity, kindness and giving, sharing and involvement.

This book is one of my greatest ever achievements and another example of a form of spirituality. I have been so driven and motivated to share my journey to help inspire others that I have found the whole process enjoyable and rewarding. This is a great example of spirituality. Writing the book isn't the spiritual bit, having the desire to want to help people is, and that was something that I had been missing in my life without even knowing it.

I always used to wonder why I never felt fully satisfied. When I got a new TV I would be thinking about the next thing I wanted to buy, or when I got back from a two-week holiday I would feel like I needed another one. That's all because I was conditioned that way and that was just how we have been brought up. But being spiritually aware offers a level of gratitude just for existing on this planet that you could never experience from any "thing" and, by giving back to others, I started to feel much more whole.

If I could summarise what spirituality has done for me, I would say it's offered me something that nobody or no "thing" could offer and that is wholeness. I now feel part of this world, literally part of it, connected with every person I come into contact with. It gives me compassion towards others as I can now look at everyone running around like headless chickens in this mad world trying desperately to make themselves happy with more money, bigger houses, nicer cars, but they are on an impossible journey. There is a great quote from Peter Crone, who is someone I admire greatly, which says, "True happiness is the absence of the search for happiness." I think that perfectly sums up what I am trying to explain.

Now I find myself at a really exciting time of my life, because I am aware of what spirituality is and my journey is just getting started. I am making the choice to practise meditation every day in a bid to unplug my senses from the world in which I live and just feel a sense of connection with the universe. Apart from that, I don't spend hours on spiritual courses or reading book after book on spirituality, I take myself for long walks and sometimes I'll even have a chat with the sky. I focus on the love I have for myself and others, I am building on my relationships day by day, and I am grateful. These are the main components of spirituality that I practise, and they offer a level of peace and fulfilment that nothing has ever come close to in my lifetime.

I want to help others; I want to build a business that is focused on helping others. There are so many challenges I want to take part in and raise as much money for charity as possible. I want to do my bit to help try and save this wonderful planet of ours, I want to bring my children up to be aware of the world and make their own choices about their future with an informed education.

SPIRITUAL AWARENESS – BETTER YOU

Spirituality is one of the most important tools we have available to us, if not THE most important. The problem is that not many people understand what it really is, and it often gets thrown in the same bucket as religion and that is the end of the conversation. The thing is it's not religion, religion is about a group of people that follow a particular story, meaning that it can be very divisive when different religious beliefs cross paths. Spirituality is seeing every being as part of the same universe, on the same team and all connected with each other. Working with the universe to reach your higher self and unlock the infinite field of possibility.

In this modern era, people have evolved to be connected to things rather than themselves, seeing themselves as the things they own or the places they work, rather than the soul they are born into the world as. Spirituality provides a different perspective, suggesting that there is more to life than what people experience on a sensory and physical level. The amazing thing about spirituality is that when you pull yourself away from the state of want and need and start to live in a state of love and gratitude, then everything you ever want will come to you anyway. You just need to keep the vision clear and keep working hard on becoming your best self, it is that simple.

You only usually become aware of a spiritual awakening once you are taking care of yourself mentally and physically, which is exactly what happened to me. You may find that in the form of wanting to learn about something random or wanting to educate yourself on the ways of the world, or wanting to be close to nature, or wanting to give back to the world. If you are reading this and have experienced or are experiencing some level of spiritual awakening the chances are you are looking after your mind and body, whereas if you are neglecting your body and mind then you will need to keep pushing through the earlier chapters of this book and let your spirituality come to you.

Once you start to appreciate the world around you and feel connected to everyone and everything, rather than divisive and separated, you will want to give back to the world in some way. Once you start the process of giving back, you will really start to feel the benefits of becoming more spiritual and you will also feel as though you are able to see the world through a lens of gratitude, but you will also be able to see how chaotic it is, how competitive it is and how everyone is destroying themselves and the planet with limited awareness, all chasing that infinite horizon that will never be achieved.

The more work you do on moving on from your past and letting go of your limiting beliefs, the more you start to separate your mind from your soul and that is what makes the magic happen. By becoming more spiritual, the universe will guide you onto the path of purpose. You will receive signs of encouragement and feel a sense of inner confidence when making decisions about your future. You simply need to do the right thing, make the right decisions and, most importantly, trust and have faith that the universe always has your back.

ACTION

- Truly understand what spirituality is, it's magical.
- See that we are all connected to each other and nature.
- Help other people that need it.
- Practise gratitude often.
- Become more mindful and appreciative of nature and the world around you.

MEDITATION – BETTER ME

Sitting still has never been one of my strong points. I struggled as a kid, and I struggle more as an adult. I had been living with the mentality that in order to succeed in life you needed to work harder than everyone else. Ingrained in me throughout my life was that those who sit still get left behind. Thankfully, I pulled myself out of that dick swinging mentality and found the benefits of self-care and spirituality, both of which arguably take a stronger mindset than hard graft.

I always wanted to work in the big city and challenge myself amongst the best in my profession, working long hours and focusing only on the day ahead of me. I was living on autopilot for years, trapped in my self-made chaotic life, never looking back and never having an understanding or appreciation for the present moment. Living that way was exhausting, but it was all I knew, and it brought with it a good level of success, or what I thought was success, but in reality, I guess I mean things?

I never really had a view on meditation, but I guess if I did it would have been similar to my view on spirituality in general: incense sticks burning and crystals catching the light whilst sitting cross-legged on a rustic old mat, humming away into some other world that may or may not exist. It was never something that interested me, but my personal development led me unwillingly in the direction of spirituality and meditation in particular. I started to explore and understand the benefits of meditation and how it works to complement the general upward trajectory I was looking to achieve in myself. It seemed that the benefits far outweighed the effort, so I decided to give it a go. After all, why not? I can sit still, close my eyes and do nothing, it can't be that hard!

But I didn't even know where to start. There are so many different types of meditations, I had so many questions, what to do, when to do it, for how long? Fortunately, there is so much information available online to help understand it all, so I just absorbed myself into it and sponged up as much information as I could in the hope of finding some kind of beginner's guide. I found a few apps that promised the experience and benefits of meditation that can be done on the move, which was perfect for my busy city life, but despite trying them out a few times, they just didn't seem to work for me. I kept getting distracted, I couldn't concentrate, and I ended up getting frustrated with it and giving up.

It was always niggling at me to get started with it again, but I really couldn't see the value of it. I made that classic human mistake of saying that it must work better for other people, it doesn't work for me. A classic example of a limiting belief. My next attempt didn't happen until months later when I decided to give guided meditations a go. They appealed to me because I could do them in the comfort of my own home. All I had to do was put some earphones in, lay back and relax. Another appeal was that I could choose from a selection of topics, like it was some kind of menu. What I chose to listen to depended on the mood I was in that day. The list went on forever; if I was feeling anxious, I searched guided meditation for anxiety, or if I wanted to work on my spiritual connection I typed in guided meditation for spiritual connection, you get the picture!

The guided meditation process involves some peaceful music playing in the background throughout, then you have someone talk over the music giving you instructions on what to think about, how to breathe or where to place your attention. It's pretty straightforward and you can't really go too far wrong, unless you start thinking about something completely trivial and forget what you are supposed to be thinking about; that definitely happened to me a few times when I started, but that's all part of the process. I did these guided meditations every day for a few weeks and definitely felt a benefit from doing them. They were pretty easy, really convenient and I felt like I was unplugging myself from the outside world and tuning into this new internal one that I had never consciously connected with before.

After a while, I wanted to step it up a gear and add some variety into the practice. I wanted to go it alone and leave the companionship of the guide behind. I just wanted to sit with myself in silence and observe what happened. I felt like guided meditations were an amazing introductory tool into the world of meditation, or perfect if I felt like I wanted to feel a certain way, but I was intrigued to see what I had in my mind without the guidance of someone else.

I wanted to move into the land of self-discovery and try the technique of mindfulness meditation; this form of meditation seemed to be the most popular from what I had observed. Mindful meditation involves sitting comfortably in a cross-legged position, closing your eyes and focusing on your breath. When your mind starts to wander, all you have to do is bring the attention back to the breath. Sounds simple. The purpose of this version of meditation is to slow down the thoughts and observe them without judgement. It was exactly the same process as the visualisation work I had already done, just without the visualisation part.

The first time I tried it, I made sure that the environment was perfect and the kids were in bed as I didn't want any distractions or any risk of them bursting through the door. I sat upright, cross-legged on my bed and took a few deep breaths in and out, in and out, in and out and then closed my eyes. I had watched plenty of different tutorials previously, so I knew exactly what I needed to do, but as soon as my eyes closed and I started to relax, my mind seemed to wake up and get the party started. It was chaos in there. I was having what seemed like hundreds of thoughts all firing away at me one after the other. It was so hard to even keep up with it, let alone to observe them, and bring my focus back to the breath, I had no chance.

I went back and tried again the following day, following the same process and the same techniques. This time it felt better and the thoughts that raced around my mind started to slow down much quicker than before. I could go into my visualisation process normally, but I struggled with not having anything to think about. My mind was like a wild animal being told to stay still. This went on for days and weeks afterwards, but the more I practised, the better I became and the more I started to master my mind rather than my mind mastering me, which was solid progress.

My thoughts mainly consisted of day-to-day considerations like what I am having for dinner or analysing the week at work I had ahead of me. But every now and again I would experience the most random thoughts about people I had forgotten existed. It was such an interesting experience I just wanted more and more of it. Day after day I practised until it all started to slow down a bit and I felt like I had a bit more control over the situation. My confidence started to grow and my ability to isolate each thought alone, observe it and let it go grew stronger each time. I had read that the muscles in your mind are just like the muscles in your body, the more you use them the stronger they become, so practice and repetition were really important in order to maximise the benefits of it, but also to fully enjoy it.

After only a couple of weeks I started to really feel the benefits of my meditation, I felt calm and relaxed, like I had been relieved of any stress in my body. That put me in a great mood and really helped me make the right choices throughout the day. I started to eat healthier, exercise more and generally feel better as a person. It also seemed to help me sleep better too. Don't get me wrong, not every meditation is wonderful and enlightening, sometimes it just didn't seem to work for me, I had too much going on and I was trying to force myself to do it, just adding to the stress I already had in my mind, but I never regretted doing it and I always hear that there is no such thing as a bad meditation, a bit like they say about working out. Sometimes it's perfect and it feels amazing, other times it can be terrible, but it's the consistency in turning up that moves you forward.

A good meditation is really incredible. I have had so many great meditations now that I am a bit more experienced and when you get a good one you feel something inside you that is off the chart, almost orgasmic. I have cried tears of joy on several occasions, just purely from the connection that I experience with myself. Now when I think about going to meditate, I get excited, sometimes a little too excited, but hey that's my personality, but I really enjoy it and the benefits of it are extraordinary.

The level of confidence I now have with meditation is significantly higher than it's ever been and continues to grow with each experience I have. But with that confidence also comes a level of trust that is so important. Because what trust does is it enables me to surrender to the experience, the universe, the moment, the greater force of nature or whatever you want to call it. I am now able to let them take over and take me in the direction they want. Control is not something us humans like to relinquish, and surrender is a word that scares the shit out of most people, but it's only now I am at that place I can see it for myself and experience the deeper state of meditation that was previously being blocked.

One of the biggest things that prevented me from previously starting to meditate was fear, fear of not knowing how to do it but mainly fear of knowing what lives inside my head. It's the unknown that often scares us, right? But the more you practise, the more you learn that meditation is never something to fear, far from it. There are too many benefits that I have experienced, it would be pointless to list them all, so perhaps an easier way of describing it would be to say that I think it's had a positive impact in every area of my life. The one thing I think I can say is that it pulled me out of my crazy world and gave me the ability to observe what was happening and reflect on the lifestyle that I am living every day. It helped me to confirm that I wasn't living an authentic life, I was addicted to the crazy long days at work and the chaotic environment I had created, and I had become this person that wasn't aligned with who I really am.

I was now able to climb out of the jar and read the label, and I didn't like what I saw. Previously my purpose had been about myself, doing better in my career, to buy bigger and better things for myself, but now all I want to do is help other people and go beyond myself. All I want to do is be in a position of service. I need to look after myself and respect my body so that I can go and help as many people all around the world as I can to live a happy, healthy life. All of that became clear the more I was meditating. I had become a victim of today's world of overstimulation, competitiveness and a win-at-all-cost mentality, but now I was able to realign myself and make major life choices that would change my world significantly.

Meditation now forms part of my everyday routine, it keeps me aligned with my true self, it takes me out of the hustle and bustle of my daily life, it forces me to sit in the present moment, it gives me a feeling of time and freedom that I find so helpful in dealing with any stressful situations that may occur during the day. But also, I can honestly say, I fucking love it, my life is so much better now and meditation has a big part to play in that. The most exciting thing is that meditation is a journey, and I am just getting started. I cannot wait to see what experiences I have with meditation in the future, I just know that it's going to be an amazing journey.

MEDITATION – BETTER YOU

We have evolved into these hyperactive beings that are constantly stimulated in one way or another and our mind is processing at such a high speed that our need to use mindfulness and meditation has never been stronger. So why don't we all do it? Well, we are hyperactive beings that are constantly stimulated, and we are addicted to that stimulation. The thought of sitting still is something most of us wouldn't comprehend and even when we become intrigued by it, there is always a reason why now isn't the right time to do it. Social media, Netflix, alcohol, whatever the convenient short-term fix is, it will always be there to tempt you away from doing something that's truly beneficial.

It is such a shame because these lazy, short-term powerhouses make it easy for people to do the same thing every day, which results in the same results every day, ultimately all having a negative effect on your physical and mental health. Anything that takes even the smallest amount of effort gets pushed out of the way in the process and meditation falls into that category, the same as exercise, fitness and nutrition. But there is always a way to get started and the beautiful thing about meditation is that you only require a few minutes a day to get started.

My advice is to not over-complicate meditation. I spent weeks and months trying to find out exactly what to do, when the best time to do it is, what the different types are called, etc., but forget that and just give something a go. I would suggest starting with a guided meditation, which you can get for free anywhere. I like to use YouTube for mine, that way you can also see how long they are and hand pick the kind of meditation you are looking to do (and they are free). There are also free apps such as Headspace and Calm that are a great way of starting and you can even do it on the move. These are successful for millions of people all over the world, so don't be put off by my lack of connection.

Start to experiment with mindful meditation when you get a bit more confident. Your experiences will differ each time, sometimes you will struggle to bring your attention back to your breath and your mind will just continuously wander, other times you will have a really deep experience where you feel so light you could be floating. It's a moving landscape all of the time and the most important thing to do is allow each experience to happen, welcome it in, don't fight it, just surrender to it and you will experience significant benefits in all areas of your life.

The fast-paced, swipe culture, chaotic world that we live in today is creating a generation of stressed beings crippled with depression about their past and anxiety about their future, making millions of people sick. My hope is that rather than opt for a pill that will mask the problem, more and more people start to look at a more natural remedy such as meditation.

The benefits to meditation literally counteract stress, anxiety and depression. Meditation puts you in the present moment and allows you to come away from the noise and reset yourself. It provides you with a vantage point in which you can see yourself for who you are versus the person you are being conditioned to be.

Meditation is one of the most exciting parts of my journey and has played a pivotal role in me becoming my better self. It really is a superpower that is largely untapped, but with the technology and information that is readily available today there has never been an easier time to get started, and let's face it, in the world we are living in, there has also never been a better time to focus on our inner peace and shift our purpose towards helping the world and each other.

ACTION

- Don't overcomplicate it.
- Do it at a time that suits you when you are least stressed.
- Start off by meditating for just a few minutes, build it up gradually.
- Use an app to help get you started, or a guided meditation on YouTube.
- Consciously unplug yourself from the world around you.
- Enjoy the moment of peace and calm.

RELATIONSHIPS – BETTER ME

I have always been someone who loves being around other people. I come from a large family, I have a large group of friends spread out across the world and I work with a bunch of different people every day. I love people and I have enjoyed a variety of different relationships throughout my lifetime. I have even maintained a strong friendship with many of my school friends, which I always think is a positive reflection on the way in which I form and maintain relationships.

As I got older, I unintentionally started spending less time with my family, going off on my own adventure, starting a new life in a new place with a set of new friends. Doing it my way, making plenty of new friends along the way, some of which were transient, others friends for life. Unsurprisingly, my friendships were always formed through things in common, which is no different to how anyone forms friendships, whether it's playing football in the playground as a kid or drinking beer in the same pub as an adult, it was that something that sparked the relationship into life and still does today.

I thought that the relationship part of my life was pretty good. I mean, I had lots of friends and they generally lasted pretty well, so that was my barometer of success. That was until I started to explore the world of spirituality and my viewpoint on the subject changed significantly. Spirituality taught me that relationships and connection were vitally important in life and that they must be nurtured, maintained and require a lot of investment to flourish.

I hadn't been working very hard on maintaining any of my relationships, I had just been relying on the fact that we had something in common and the length of time we had been friends for to get us through. I was doing the bare minimum to maintain them, assuming that they wouldn't go anywhere, and more often than not they didn't. But hanging onto a relationship is vastly different to learning about what a good relationship looks and feels like. I had no idea about all of the benefits that connection and relationships could bring to my life when done correctly. I had just been content with the way they all were and never consciously thought about needing to invest in them. They just were what they were.

On reflection, many of my relationships had stagnated and a big reason for that was alcohol. Firstly, if I was hungover, I didn't want to see or speak to anyone and, secondly, drinking had slowly become the dominant reason for meeting up with the people I had relationships with. Once that happened, there was a shift from wanting to see people and connect with them, to wanting to go for a drink with that person. Subtle shift but big difference. I just associated certain friends or family members with certain places or drinks. Don't get me wrong, I had some amazing times with my friends along the way whilst drinking, but it's the beginning of the end when your relationship reaches the state of sitting in a pub or boozing in front of the TV, no matter who you are.

My spirituality had given me the desire to want to be connected and play a big part in other people's lives, but it had also taught me that I was already a complete person. That may sound a bit strange, but previously I had looked at each person I had a close relationship with as all forming a specific part of who I am, whether that's my parents, close friends or my partner, they all made up the different parts of the jigsaw puzzle that completes me. Meaning that if any of them were to leave me, die or run away then I would be left incomplete or empty. But by implying that other people complete me, I am saying I am incomplete without them, which just isn't true. That gave me a new perspective on my relationships and made me realise that they are like a supplement to a good life, two complete people adding value to each other's lives, helping to grow, develop, blossom and flourish as a partnership.

I started to realise that, as humans, we like to do what we want, go to places that we want to go at a time that suits us. There is a general bias towards our own feelings, rather than prioritising the other person's feelings. I was no different to that. I had been living my life thinking that what I think and say is the way that life should be. Although I respected my friends and family and had a great deal of love for them, at times I would become frustrated with them for not living their lives the way that I was living mine. I would judge them or perceive them as wrong if their views weren't aligned with my own. This behaviour had been happening at a subconscious level, so I didn't even realise I was doing it until I discovered this new perspective.

Now that I understand relationships, why we have them and what benefit they bring to us individually and as a species, my view has transformed. I now see all of my friends and family as such valuable people in my life. I no longer take any of them for granted and ensure that I invest as much time as I can into nurturing them. The connection I now have in every one of my relationships is in a significantly better place than ever before.

I have reconnected with old friends from years gone by and made a whole new set of friends through my social media platform, most of which I have never met but I value them as much as I value any of my relationships. Technology has transformed the way I communicate with people, and I really feel the value in every relationship I now have in my life. I consciously work to maintain them and try to be as active as I can to ensure I play my part with all these truly meaningful relationships. I am so excited to have discovered the amazing benefits of connection and relationships, I feel as though I am starting again with more enthusiasm than ever before.

RELATIONSHIPS – BETTER YOU

What I want you to realise is that relationships should be a supplement to your life, they should add value, elevate your mood, stimulate your growth and help you to flourish as a person. But what's really important to realise is that you were born alone as a beautiful creation from the universe, destined for your own unique journey that lies ahead of you. The people that you meet along the way will add to that experience, but they will never complete you, you are already complete.

By thinking other people complete who you are, whether that is your sister, best friend or husband, implies that you are incomplete, which in turn puts a great deal of pressure on that relationship. When you realise that you are already a complete human being and do not require anyone or anything else to complete you, it changes the way in which you look at relationships. It removes the pressure and brings back the positivity factor.

I now look at relationships like agreements, two people agreeing to form a relationship with each other and committing to help each other grow and flourish in life; someone to share things with, someone to talk to and someone to experience life with. Relationships are supposed to be fun and adventurous, whilst being deep and emotional. They require a lot of work to maintain, but if they get the attention they need, they are the most amazing gifts you could ask for.

One of the missing parts I see so often is the understanding that both people are equal in the relationship. We have a tendency to think of ourselves as being the more dominant one, the one who is right and the one who is the priority, but what we overlook is the fact that the other person or people have gone through their own journey and experiences and deserve an equal level of respect. A lot of the time relationships break down because the egos clash heads and, rather than communicating with compassion and acceptance, we defend our beliefs with anger and frustration. We fail to realise that if we would have lived their life in the exact way that they have, trodden the same path, seen the same things and experienced the same conditions then we would behave the same way they are.

What people like to do is run away if they feel emotionally triggered by something someone says, rather than see those triggers as revealing where you are not at peace or where you have your own insecurity. How often does your friend or partner really piss you off by saying something trivial, but it really fires you up? Then it causes an argument, which usually results in one of two things happening, either they say sorry for saying something trivial that has provoked your insecurity, or you break off the relationship and start over. Now in scenario number one where they say sorry, that's not right because they are just saying what they are saying, it's you that has been provoked by it, therefore it's your insecurity to work on. In scenario number two where you break off the relationship, what happens six months later when your next partner or friend says something trivial, and it sparks you off again? You will just be running in circles until you realise that friendships and relationships will never be perfect, they will always require a lot of maintenance, and you have just as much responsibility as the other person or people in it with you.

Find the right people for you in your life and, once you have found them, work hard to nurture them. If they trigger you in any way, then see that as golden treasure for you to work on freeing yourself from your own constraints. Your relationships with your family will always go through as many hard times as they will good times, that's just part of being human, but if someone in your family does something that you are upset by, speak to them with love and compassion. They will be doing the best job they can with the upbringing they experienced, the conditioning they had and the life that they live. Compassion and acceptance are always the solutions. It's a lot easier to say it than to do it because our big old egos like to get in the way and make sure we are right, but it's a lot better to be kind than right.

ACTION

- Appreciate the value that relationships have in your life.
- Work hard to maintain and develop them.
- Listen more, talk less.
- Utilise the online world to keep in touch.
- With your knowledge of the mind, you will understand people better and can bring a sense of compassion to them and appreciate that everyone is a result of their conditioning.

SELF-LOVE – BETTER ME

Losing Rocco hurt me so much that it left me angry and for some reason I was angry at myself, as if it was my fault and I could have prevented it. I felt the need to punish myself by abusing my own body and always keeping busy so that my thoughts wouldn't be able to surface. I was stuck in a pool of bitter frustration, which raged inside me like wildfire, and the only way I knew how to channel it was to do everything harder than ever before, work harder, party harder and punish myself harder.

At my lowest point, I had no regard for my health or well-being whatsoever. I was barely sleeping, working flat out, drinking every day, doing very little exercise, using coffee to get me through the day and drugs to get me through the night. Sometimes I would go days without eating anything, other days I would eat everything I could get my hands on. It was a fast-paced, punishing lifestyle, focusing more on self-harm than self-love. I used work and socialising as distractions from my own feelings. My theory was that if I just kept busy all the time, I could just ignore all the feelings that were locked deep inside of me, building and multiplying as the weeks went on.

I didn't know what self-love was and, even if I did, I wouldn't have thought I was worthy of receiving it. At that time in my life, my understanding of self-love would have been treating myself to a few beers and a curry, taking the family on holiday, or indulging in a new TV. None of which are self-love whatsoever. But because that was my understanding of self-love, that also became my default way of showing love to my family, by giving them things rather than time. Which ultimately played a big part in losing it all.

Once I was on the path of recovery and had plugged myself into the spiritual connection switchboard, I was able to see the obvious error in my ways. I am determined to reverse the years of physical abuse and damage that I inflicted on myself by prioritising everything that I have discussed in this book. I am raising my vibration by exercising regularly, eating nutritious food packed with as many nutrients as possible, keeping hydrated every day, prioritising sleep every night. I couldn't believe that even through all of the years of punishment I had given my body, it still came back to life and made me feel incredible in such a short amount of time; that was another real moment of appreciation and gratitude.

With the physical changes in full flow, I was feeling great, but it was the spiritual part of my journey that took me to a new level of self-love. I was able to appreciate life for the miracle that it is, and I had a newfound appreciation for how lucky we are to be part of it and how amazing we are as humans. I started to shift my perspective from one of lack and want, into one of gratitude and love, which made me feel connected to the universe in a way that I had never experienced.

The routine of self-love began by meditating every day, allowing myself time with my own thoughts. I started to use my journal daily to reflect on how I'm feeling and how aligned I am feeling with myself. I started to practise gratitude daily and sometimes multiple times during the day. I spent time walking and being amongst nature. I started to use creativity as a way of expressing myself every day, sometimes it's writing, often it's cooking and other times it's drawing or painting with the kids.

I was becoming a different person, I felt connected to something much greater than myself, and it felt amazing. The more I was investing in myself, the more connected I felt. I could feel myself vibrating at a level I had never felt before. I started to observe how many other people in the world were behaving in the same way that I had done previously, blissfully unaware of the damage they were doing to their body, trapped in the stresses of life, stuck in a state of suffering, and desperately searching for that relief through some form of external source such as drinking or overworking. Now that my own cup was full, I was able to start writing this book and launching my own social platform in the hope of being able to help as many people as possible break free from their internal prison that I was all too familiar with.

SELF-LOVE – BETTER YOU

Self-love is NOT about having a big ego or being narcissistic, it's accepting who you are and investing in your own well-being and happiness. People often think that self-love is about running a hot bath and putting on a face mask, but that's actually called self-care. Some people think self-love is eating a whole tub of ice cream in front of a movie, but that's actually called greed! But in all seriousness, these things are great, but they are all going to make you feel good in the moment and not really have much of a long-term effect – or in the case of the ice cream, eating it will have a negative long-term effect.

Materialistic things will never provide you with anything more than a quick dopamine hit, that is it. Far too many people in the world are searching externally for happiness that is only found within. It really is as simple as that and, now that I can see it, I see it everywhere in a variety of different forms, some more controversial than others, but it's the same problem, addiction. That short-sighted, quick fix hit of dopamine, whether it's buying clothes online, drinking alcohol, having sex, doing drugs, they are all different variations of the same thing and they will all give you no long-term happiness. All they do is put you in a cycle of addiction that's extremely hard to break out of.

Self-love is about looking after your mind, body and soul and giving yourself whatever you need to flourish. By going for a long walk in the woods you will be lighting up your senses and connecting with nature, by moving your body you will be burning calories and clearing your mind, and by eating a nutritious diet you will give yourself more energy throughout the day and enhance your mood.

Sit alone with your thoughts for ten minutes per day. Call it meditation, mindfulness or just sitting down, it doesn't matter, just do it. The mental benefits you experience will have a positive knock-on effect to the physical benefits too. This gives you time to reset and realign with your soul and keep you on track to your future vision.

Practise gratitude daily. Once you start to be grateful for everything you have in your life and stop chasing the material horizon, you will have a very different perspective on life and will become much more relaxed and appreciative. That can only be good for you.

One thing I have learnt is that you can only love other people at the level you love yourself. Once you start to practise self-love, your relationships with friends, family and colleagues will improve almost immediately because you are coming from a place of love internally. You will also set the standard for how other people treat you. Like the quote says, "Treat yourself the way you want others to treat you."

You would have heard of the analogy, 'is your glass half full or half empty?' Well, in my opinion, you need to put all of your efforts into filling the thing up rather than worrying about how you look at it. Once you have a cup that is full, what happens? It starts to overflow. That's when you can help others. So, although some people may think that self-love is a selfish act, it's all about getting yourself to an optimal state, so then you will be in a position to help others.

ACTION

- Believe in yourself and take responsibility for your own life.
- Believe in your vision.
- Connect with the higher power.
- Practise gratitude, shift your perspective.
- Keep your vibration high.
- Fill up the cup.

CONCLUSION

I hope you have enjoyed reading this book as much as I enjoyed writing it. I am so passionate about sharing this formula with the world as I know for myself that it works.

So many people in this beautiful world are trapped in a cycle of life, thinking that the aim is to survive and that they are aren't worthy of any kind of happiness or success. What I have learned and what many more people are starting to realise is that is complete bullshit. Every single person is put on this planet to make a difference and it's up to you to find out what that is.

Everything starts with you, you must look after yourself, respect yourself and love yourself before you can help others. If you can master your mind, take care of your body and connect with your soul, you are putting yourself on the path to freedom and enlightenment.

Life isn't about buying nice cars or having nice things, it's about playing your part to help other people in the world, it's about being grateful for every day that you are lucky enough to live on this beautiful planet and setting the example to the generations ahead.

Unfortunately, we have been conditioned into being very egotistical beings, who are often greedy, selfish and ungrateful. But the world is changing, and people are starting to wake up and realise that isn't okay and it is certainly not why we are here. We are all connected through energy and, if we work together, we can make this world a much happier place, and leave it in a much better condition than the one we inherited.

PERSONAL AND PROFESSIONAL AMBITION

My ambitions in life have completely changed over the last few years. I used to think that I wanted a life filled with material goods, big houses and fancy holidays. But now I dream of a life filled with love, freedom and true happiness.

I have realised that life isn't about working long hours and getting stressed out, longing for the weekend or my next holiday, living from pay cheque to pay cheque. Life is so much more than that, it's about doing what makes me happy, finding things that I am passionate about, exploring new parts of the world, trying new things, making new connections, and helping people along the way, that's living a life of purpose.

Since going sober, I now feel as though I am on the right path. I am really enjoying helping people to change their relationship with alcohol, which ultimately changes their whole life. By removing one thing, they gain back everything.

But my biggest ambition of them all is to make my family proud of me, not because of what I do or who I help, but for who I am and what I stand for. Without alcohol in my life, I am able to offer my family the best version of me every single day. I hope that by living a happy, healthy and ambitious lifestyle I will encourage my children to do the same.

I want my wife and children to be as proud of me as I know my boy in the sky is.

A life filled with love is a life well lived.

MORE OF ME

🌐 www.betterlifeguy.com

📷 better_life_guy

f better life guy

Made in United States
North Haven, CT
07 March 2022

16876770R00143